STONE WALL

RAILS

WALL AND RAILS

DOUBLE OXER

HULLO!

BONJOUR

HALLO!

HOLA!

THE BEST OF
Girl
Annual
1952~1959

DENIS GIFFORD

KYA HAL HAI

GUTEN TAG

ЗАРАСТВУЙТЕ

HAERE MAI

DZIENDOBRY

CIAO!

Webb & Bower

This book
belongs to

First published in Great Britain 1990 by
Webb & Bower (Publishers) Limited
5 Cathedral Close, Exeter, Devon EX1 1EZ

Distributed by the Penguin Group
Penguin Books Ltd, Registered Offices: Harmondsworth
Middlesex, England
Penguin Books Australia Ltd, Ringwood, Victoria, Australia
Penguin Books Canada Ltd, 2801 John Street, Markham, Ontario
Canada L3R 1B4
Penguin Books (NZ) Ltd, 182–190 Wairau Road, Auckland 10, New Zealand

Designed by Vic Giolitto

© Fleetway Publications, London 1990
Introduction and compilation Copyright © 1990 Denis Gifford

British Library Cataloguing in Publication Data

Best of Girl annual, 1952–1959.
1. Girls' annuals in English
I. Gifford, Denis, 1927–
082
ISBN 0–86350–394–2

The text is set in Gill Sans
Typeset in Great Britain by P&M Typesetting Ltd, Exeter, Devon

Colour reproduction by Peninsular Repro Services Ltd, Exeter, Devon

Printed and bound in Hong Kong by Mandarin Offset

CONTENTS

INTRODUCTION

'The New Super Colour Weekly For Every Girl' they headlined it, the Reverend Marcus Morris and his team, and number one was stacked high on British newsagents' counters on Friday the second of November, 1951. If you missed it, you are either too young or you haven't got a brother. For as they cunningly subtitled it, *Girl* was 'Sister Paper to *Eagle*', and half a page of that well-read boys' comic was given over to a very exciting advert. 'Today's the Great Day for All Girls!' trumpeted the topline, 'Go to your newsagent and buy your first copy of *Girl*, your own paper, this minute, or you may be disappointed!'

An advertisement for girls to read in a boys' comic? An historic moment indeed, for Morris and his staff knew something that few of their million or so bare-kneed readers realised. Girls all over the country were taking sneaky peeks at their brothers' weekly *Eagle*, and indeed some were even buying it for themselves! Editor Morris revealed all in his opening address to his readers:

'Here's wishing you many enjoyable hours of good *Girl* reading. For a long time, we, who have been responsible for producing *Eagle*, have been wanting to produce another paper especially for girls – and we have had hundreds of letters asking us to do so. At last we have managed to find a team of artists and writers, to fix up the printing and buy the paper [there were austerity problems in those first years of the New Elizabethan Age] – and here we are … Please write in to me and tell me your views, as that's the only way I can know for certain what sort of things you like. The more letters I get from you the better!'

Well, Morris was certainly asking for it – and evidently got it, for although to the eye of a professionally-interested male party such as myself, *Girl* appeared an exciting comic, it seems I – and Marcus Morris – was wrong! Mentally switch yourself back to 1951 and consider if you will the principal line-up of *Girl's* strip cartoon attractions.

Kitty Hawke and her All Girl Air Crew: 'Join in the hair-raising exploits of Kitty Hawke, daring girl pilot, and her gay all-girl air crew.' Shrugging aside the obvious cue for a liberated laugh, Kitty was an obvious doppelganger for *Eagle's* own front page hero, Dan Dare. Suspecting that science-fiction would be too strong a subject for a Fifties girl to swallow, artist Ray Bailey set his green-capped upswept blonde firmly in the present, as she cried 'Well, here we are again, gang, one more job chalked up to prove to Dad that we can operate his planes as efficiently as the glorious males!' One

glorious male in the ground staff cried, 'Kitty Hawke's the only pilot I know who can do a roll in a Tadcaster!'

Captain Starling: 'Sail over the stormy seas in the Kestrel with the courageous Starling in her quest to find her father on the other side of the world.'

Anne Mullion: 'The colour, romance and adventure of the 18th century is brought to you in the story of the Silver Sabot.'

Judy and Pat: 'Who stole the school cups? Who was the queer old woman on the beach? The Mystery of Pine Ridge School will keep you guessing.'

Well, none of them proved to be any reader's favourite, and nor did Candy Maitland, Jacky the Centre Page Girl, or Penny Wise, Private Detective. In fact, the only survivor of the first *Girl* – who was still going strong in the last *Girl* – was Lettice Leefe, the Greenest Girl in the School! Drawn in full colour by John Ryan, the only cartoonist to contribute to both *Eagle* and *Girl* simultaneously, the Pride of St Addledegga's survived through not only the thirteen year run of *Girl* (664 editions), but even the fatal incorporation with a lesser comic, *Princess*, for three more years. You will find her in this souvenir volume, of course, but not I fear Judy, Pat, Anne, nor even Kitty Hawke.

By the time Marcus Morris came to edit the first *Girl Annual*, which was published in the autumn of 1952, Kitty and all the Girl Crew had flown off into that wide blue yonder reserved for unsuccessful comic heroes and heroines. It was Morris' call for 'the more letters the better' that did it. Readers responded in their thousands, proving that what your young female mind of the Fifties wanted was not high-flying pilotesses, teenage 'tecs and girl skippers, but the traditional schoolgirls' fiction that they had hitherto been reading in *Girls' Crystal* and *School Friend*. In came schoolgirls Wendy and Jinx, Chums of the Fourth Form; Robbie of Red Hall, orphan heiress among the hieland heather; Jala the Jungle Girl, Belle of the Ballet, Susan of St. Bride's – junior soap-opera starring boarders, dancers, nurses and ponies.

After 1959, under new management at Longacre Press, the *Annual*, like the comic, changed in character and quality. This compilation ignores those later years. But we have not ignored those other stars of the Fifties, the show-business personalities who were interviewed especially for *Girl Annual*, so as well as favourite and fondly-remembered fictional figures, here are the lovely Vivien Leigh, and the perhaps even lovelier (to *Girl* readers) Dirk Bogarde, Kenneth More, Richard Burton and Dennis Lotis. Ah, those were the days!

STARLING AND THE CHERUB, WITH THEIR COUSIN HUMP AND THE NEGRO HELMSMAN SAM, ARE CRUISING IN THE *KESTREL* OFF THE CHANNEL ISLES ONE SUMMER EVENING — WHEN SUDDENLY —

Lettice Leefe — CRIME AT ST ADDLEDEGGA'S — *The Greenest Girl in School!*

GIRLS! THE MOST TERRIBLE THING HAS HAPPENED!! THE SILVER SPORTS TROPHY HAS VANISHED!! I HOPE IT IS JUST A FOOLISH PRANK....

...BUT TO MAKE CERTAIN, I HAVE ENGAGED A FAMOUS DETECTIVE TO INVESTIGATE --- MR. HARRIS TWEED! -- HE ARRIVES THIS AFTERNOON

GOSH!! HARRIS TWEED! HE'S EVER SO CLEVER - I DO HOPE HE'LL FIND IT!

AND SO, THAT AFTERNOON....

SUCH AN HONOUR MR. TWEED AND I'M SURE YOU'LL SOLVE OUR LITTLE MYSTERY EASILY!!

HA, HA, YES! JUST A MATTER OF TAKING A LOOK ROUND YOU KNOW.

WHAT AN *IMPORTANT* LOOKING MAN! - AND HIS ASSISTANT LOOKS RATHER NICE, TOO.

PERHAPS YOU COULD TAKE ME ON A TOUR OF THE SCHOOL FIRST, EH?

DELIGHTED!! WE'LL START RIGHT AWAY, SHALL WE! THIS....

IS OUR GREENHOUSE - THE LATEST TYPE, OF COURSE! AND HERE IS MR. BLUGGINS - THE PORTER...

VERY BUSY CULTIVATING ...WHAT *IS* IT YOU'RE CULTIVATING, BLUGGINS?

MUSTARD & CRESS 'M.

OOH, I SAY, LOOK! LOOK AT MR. TWEED! HE'S SPOTTED SOMETHING

NO NEED TO GO ANY FURTHER! INCREDIBLE THO' IT MAY SEEM, I HAVE SOLVED THE PROBLEM.

SEE THAT BUNDLE ON THE GUTTER UP THERE! I SUSPECT THAT *THAT* IS THE MISSING TROPHY.

BRILLIANT, MR. TWEED. HOW *DO* YOU DO IT? WE MUST FETCH A LADDER AT ONCE!

OH CRIKEY - THAT'S THE BUNDLE I CHUCKED OUT OF THE DORMITORY WINDOW - THAT BAD MEAT PIE I COULDN'T EAT! OH, I WONDER IF THAT BOY WOULD HELP ME?

PLEASE - CAN YOU HELP? I *MUST* GET THAT BUNDLE BEFORE THEY DO. IT'S NOT THE TROPHY, BUT I'LL GET INTO TERRIBLE TROUBLE IF MISS FROTH FINDS IT!

SUSAN FOLLOWS THE CLOTHES-LINE

HALLO! I'M SUSAN.

OLD-FASHIONED CLOTHES IN PICTURES AND PLAYS — PERHAPS WORN THEM AS 'FANCY DRESS'.

YOUR CLOTHES WOULD SURPRISE CHILDREN OF THE PAST MORE THAN THEIRS WOULD SURPRISE YOU FOR YOU HAVE SEEN · · · · · · · · · · · ·

NOWADAYS FASHIONS CHANGE QUICKLY. THINK OF WEARING MOTHER'S FROCK OR GRANDMOTHER'S!

TO THE BOYS AND GIRLS WHO WORE THEM EVERY DAY SUCH CLOTHES WERE AS ORDINARY AS YOURS ARE TO YOU.

1896   1925

IN ANCIENT TIMES THE SAME STYLES WERE WORN FOR CENTURIES.

EGYPT   1450 B·C

Slashing came from Germany.

Padding from Spain.

Lace from the Low Countries.

AS CIVILISATION SPREAD AND PEOPLES OF DIFFERENT LANDS MET, EXCHANGED IDEAS AND TRADED WITH ONE ANOTHER, FASHIONS CHANGED MORE OFTEN.

ALL SORTS OF THINGS INFLUENCE CLOTHES. FOR INSTANCE :-

ARTIFICIAL SILK   NYLON   RAYON

SCIENCE GIVES NEW FABRICS.

SPORT POPULARISED SHORTS.

1861

ITALIAN POLITICS GAVE US THE GARIBALDI SHIRT.

1905

AND, AS ALWAYS, THE ROYAL NAVY HAS DONE ITS SHARE!

UNTIL LESS THAN 200 YEARS AGO CHILDREN DRESSED VERY LIKE GROWN-UPS

SAXON

SOMETIMES THEIR CLOTHES WERE SERVICEABLE · · · ·

···· SOMETIMES PICTURESQUE ··

PLANTAGENET

YORKIST

··· SOMETIMES STARTLING ···

··SOMETIMES DOWNRIGHT IDIOTIC····

TUDOR

STUART

···OFTEN BEAUTIFUL·····

GEORGIAN

···BUT EVEN MORE OFTEN UNCOMFORTABLE!

LITTLE BOYS TOO YOUNG TO BE DRESSED AS MEN WERE DRESSED AS WOMEN.

1595

1615

AT TIMES THEY MANAGED TO LOOK QUITE BOYISH IN SPITE OF THEIR PETTICOATS.

1787

BUT OFTEN IT MUST HAVE BEEN HARD TO TELL A BOY FROM A GIRL.

1855

1883

1825

EVEN WHEN THEY HAD CLOTHES OF THEIR OWN LITTLE BOYS WERE MADE TO LOOK RIDICULOUS.

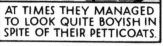

TO-DAY

UNTIL WITH THE 20TH. CENTURY, CAME ROMPER AND BUSTER SUITS.

1914

ON THE DUTCH ISLAND OF MARKEN, THE ODD CUSTOM OF DRESSING BOYS UP TO THE AGE OF SEVEN AS WOMEN, STILL SURVIVES.

A girl.

Dress of boys up to seven years of age

After ten.

Between seven and ten.

MANY PETTICOATS MAKE THE DUTCH CHILDRENS SKIRTS STAND OUT. YOUR VICTORIAN GREAT GRANDMOTHER FOUND IT EASIER TO DRAPE HER LARGE SKIRTS OVER A FRAME OF WHALEBONE, CANE OR STEEL, CALLED A CRINOLINE.

1866

100 YEARS EARLIER GEORGIANS HAD WORN HOOPS AND 200 YEARS BEFORE THAT, TUDORS HAD THEIR FARTHINGALES.

1750

1570

ABOUT 1770 BOYS AT LAST HAD STYLES OF THEIR OWN. COAT-TAILS WERE CUT OFF AND TROUSERS REPLACED BREECHES.

TO-DAY PAGES AT 'POSH' WEDDINGS SOMETIMES WEAR SIMILAR SUITS.

TOWARDS THE CLOSE OF THE 18TH. CENTURY WOMEN GAVE UP HOOPS. THEIR NEW FROCKS SUITED YOUNG GIRLS QUITE WELL.

NEVERTHELESS SHORTER SKIRTS & PANTALETTES ARRIVED EARLY IN THE FOLLOWING CENTURY.

TENNIS 1884

GIRLS INTEREST IN OUTDOOR GAMES BEGAN DURING QUEEN VICTORIA'S REIGN. AT FIRST THEY PLAYED IN 'SPORTY' VERSIONS OF THEIR WALKING DRESSES.

CRICKET 1888

HOCKEY 1893

1901

SWIMMING, OF COURSE, ALWAYS HAD ITS SPECIAL DRESS.

AS EARLY AS 1888 GIRLS OF THE ROYAL MASONIC SCHOOL DID PHYSICAL EXERCISES AND DRILL.

1900 SAW GO-AHEAD GIRLS SCHOOLS WEARING A SPECIAL DRILLING DRESS.

OLD SCHOOL UNIFORMS ARE OFTEN PICTURESQUE.

CHRIST'S HOSPITAL HORSHAM.

TO-DAY   1813

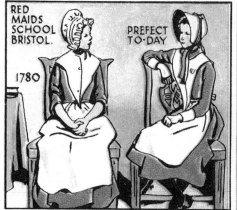

RED MAIDS SCHOOL BRISTOL.

1780

PREFECT TO-DAY

BURLINGTON SCHOOL LONDON

18TH. CENTURY

19TH. CENTURY

TROUSERS FOR GIRLS, AS YOU KNOW THEM, ARE MODERN.

ABOUT 100 YEARS AGO MRS. BLOOMER DESIGNED A VERY BAGGY KIND FOR WOMEN, BUT VERY FEW WORE THEM.

IN THE EIGHTEEN-NINETIES KNICKERBOCKERS WERE THOUGHT FASHIONABLE FOR CYCLING.

EASTERN WOMEN HAVE WORN TROUSERS FOR CENTURIES WHILST····

PERSIAN CHINESE AND TUNISIAN

by Foster-Tarrett

···IN SOME COUNTRIES, MEN WEAR SKIRTS!

GREEK

GUATEMA-LAN

& INDIAN

THE END.

Some Wild Flowers Of The Countryside

Devised and Drawn by William Wood

Birds And Animals Of The Woodland

Devised and Drawn by William Wood

Our Gracie

THE WONDERFUL STORY OF THE

MILL GIRL FROM ROCHDALE

By Alan Jenkins with illustrations by Dudley Pout

FIFTY years ago, in the Lancashire town of Rochdale, there was a fish-and-chip shop known as "Chips Sarah's." It was in Molesworth Street, nor far from the Rochdale Hippodrome. Sarah, the old lady who kept the shop, was the grandmother of a little girl who was afterwards to become known all over the world as Gracie Fields. Only she wasn't Gracie Fields in those days. She was Grace Stansfield, and she and her mother and father and brother and two sisters lived in the house above the fish-and-chip shop. "Three girls to one boy!" Gracie says now. "It wasn't fair on the lad!"

They were a happy family, poor but proud, and they got on very well together. The children never called their parents "Mum" and "Dad", and to Gracie her mother and father were always "Fred and Jinny". In spite of her fame and popularity, and the enormous amount of money she has earned, Gracie would never dream of forgetting Molesworth Street, Rochdale, and the simple kindly people among whom she spent her childhood.

Gracie, who is 54 now (and, being a straightforward person, she doesn't mind who knows it), was born on January 9, 1898.

When Gracie was a little girl, there was no radio or television: cinemas were only just beginning, with flickering silent films, and the chief treat was to be taken to the music-hall or theatre – such as the Rochdale Hippodrome, which was a very important thing in the life of the Stansfield family. They not only went regularly to the Hippodrome and enjoyed all the shows, but they sometimes got free tickets too; for Mrs Stansfield, Gracie's mother, used to do the laundry and mending for the actors, actresses and singers who came to Rochdale. And anyone who saw the family would have been glad to let Gracie's mother look after their clothes, for the Stansfield children were always clean and well turned-out, especially on Sundays and at Whitsun (which was a big celebration in Lancashire). On these special occasions Gracie and her sisters and brother were to be seen in their Sunday best – the whole family in fine velvet dresses and suits. Otherwise they were pretty much like other children, always getting their clothes torn; especially Gracie, who was often spanked for climbing on the roof to fetch a lost ball which had rolled down the slates into the gutter.

Gracie went to the local Parish Church School, and the first time she ever sang in public (as far as she can remember) was at one of the school concerts. The headmaster, Mr White, admired her enthusiasm and unselfconsciousness, but he didn't think much of her voice. "Really, Grace," he used to say, "I think you sing much too loud!" Since then, our Gracie has filled the Albert Hall and some of the world's biggest theatres, and nobody complains of not being able to hear her, so it is just as well that she took no notice of Mr White.

Rochdale's most popular cinema in those days was called Pringle's Picture Palace, and Gracie, who was well-known in Rochdale as a child entertainer, used to sing in between films. There are probably still a few people in Rochdale who remember an old playbill (and may even have kept a copy of it!) dated June 26, 1910. For that week's attraction (Pringle's Picture Palace proudly announced) was a stirring drama called "Solomon Isles", which was exciting enough; but what really drew the crowds (especially the people of Molesworth Street) was a line in thick black type: "Grace Stansfield, Rochdale's Coming Vocalist." Already, too,

Gracie was beginning to do her famous "imitations" of well-known variety stars of those far-off days (such as George Formby, father of the George Formby we know today). At twelve, Our Gracie was well on the way to becoming the great personality she is today.

"Fred" and "Jinny" were pleased at their daughter's success, and "Jinny" was sure that Gracie was going to be a great star one day. But "Fred" was doubtful. He'd seen the actors and actresses at the Hippodrome, and

show a bit more talent before he'd allow it. Meanwhile, he decided, she ought to do as nearly all the other Lancashire children did in those days – earn a steady wage by working in the cotton-mills or a factory. "Shove her in't factory," he said to his wife. He was an engineer in the same factory, and he knew the work wouldn't be too hard for a girl of twelve. But Gracie's mother argued, and in the end they determined that Gracie should have a part-time job in a cotton-mill as a "half-

A great moment for Gracie – being made a "Freeman of Rochdale", the highest honour a town can confer on one of its citizens. To celebrate the occasion Gracie rode round Rochdale on a fire engine!

some of them didn't look as if they ate enough. The theatre was an uncertain life: was the adventure of it worth the risk? For several years now Gracie had been appearing at "benefits" – weekly concerts at the working-people's clubs where she had been paid, not in money, but in "tuppenny pies". That was all right, her father thought, and he had even allowed her to tour Lancashire with a troupe of children for a shilling a week, which was good pocket money for a kid of eleven.

But the stage as a career? Ee, t'lass would have to

timer". So Gracie, in her shawl and wooden clogs, clattered to work over the cobbled streets every morning with the other "half-time" girls in Rochdale.

But she went on with her singing, and like many a music-hall star, spent a season or two in a seaside concert party – notably in "Uncle Jimmy's Jollities" at Colwyn Bay. The first song she ever sang in public was called "What makes me love you as I love you?" and it went down as well in Colwyn Bay as it had in Rochdale Parish Church schoolroom.

It was a Mr Fred Hutchings who decided Gracie's future. He saw that this hazel-eyed, auburn-haired girl with the cheeky face could be something much bigger than "Rochdale's Coming Vocalist." Gracie, now 15, wanted to be either a serious actress or an opera singer or both. Fred Hutchings changed all that. He ran a concert party called "The Cosy Corner" which played at various Lancashire seaside resorts, and especially at Lytham St Anne's. He was very smart at finding promising young performers. His pianist, for example, was a young man named Jack Hylton who, only ten years later, started a world-famous dance-orchestra and is now one of the leading theatrical managers in London.

Fred Hutchings was impressed, not merely by Gracie's singing, but still more by her ability to make people *laugh*. She was, he saw, a born comedienne. She had one particular "turn" that always brought the house down: she could play the part of an old Lancashire washerwoman! Whenever Gracie gave a serious recitation, or sang one of her serious songs, Fred Hutchings would shout: "Now do it in Lancashire!" If you have ever heard someone recite "The boy stood on the burning deck" or sing Tosti's "Because" in broad Lancashire dialect, you will know how funny Gracie could be, and how right Fred was. And Fred paid her more money than she had earned before – twenty-five shillings a week!

Not long afterwards she was earning five pounds a week – at Oldham music-hall, the manager of which, Mr Dottridge, saw a great future for this strange girl who could make her audience cry one moment and yell with laughter the next; who could sing grand opera, and then, before the applause had died down, astonish everybody by doing the splits or a couple of cartwheels!

If you were to ask Gracie Fields what she feels about the enormous success she has made of her life, and the great adventure that has brought her from clogs-and-a-shawl in Lancashire to riches and fame, she would almost certainly tell you something like this: "Ee, it isn't the money, loove. It's being able to help people, and knowing that you can make them happy, and knowing that they're glad to see you, and that you've got friends everywhere you go." Success has not spoilt her at all, and, wonderful as she is on the stage, she owes her popularity to her personality above everything else. No other variety artist is loved so well as Gracie Fields – by men and women and children in every walk of life and every country in the world. (Except, perhaps, in Russia! Recently her radio producer, Gordon Crier, was arrested by the Russians because he entered the Russian Zone by mistake while organising Gracie's tour among our troops in Germany.

Gordon Crier tried to explain that he was Gracie's producer, but the Russians just looked blank and asked: "Who is Gracie Fields?")

After the First World War, Gracie came to London for the first time. She had been popular for years in the North of England, but how would London like her? Would she be too "Lancashire" for them? She needn't have worried. Soon London too was singing her songs – "The Biggest Aspidistra in the World", "Walter, Walter, Lead me to the Altar", and "The Rochdale Hounds". If London had never heard of Rochdale, it was going to now! In the meantime, Gracie had met a theatrical producer who was destined to help her a lot on her way to fame. He was Archie Pitt, and after he had seen her act and heard her sing, he introduced himself: "My name's Pitt. You know, you're a clever girl. You and I really ought to be in partnership." Gracie thought it sounded a good idea, and soon she was playing the lead in Archie Pitt's revue "Mr Tower of London" at the old Alhambra Theatre in Leicester Square.

GRACIE was nervous as the first night of the show drew near. She had a feeling that "Mr Tower" wasn't going to be a success. And when the first night came, it looked like a complete failure. Everything seemed to go wrong. The actors forgot their lines, and bumped into pieces of scenery, some of the scene-shifters were late, and it looked like one of the worst muddles ever seen on the stage. But somehow Archie Pitt pulled the show together, and, as often happens in the theatre, a failure was turned into a roaring success. "Mr Tower" went on tour for *six years*! Which, at the time, was a record.

Gracie's songs became known everywhere – "Turn Albert's face to the wall", "When I grow too old to dream", "South American Joe" – each song so different, funny or sad or gay, but all rolled together in the same programme. Our Gracie is still the only singer who, without offending anybody, can sing a religious song like *Ave Maria* and a comic song such as *The Rochdale Hunt* one after the other! Some people think she oughtn't to do this, but Gracie's answer is: "I don't think God means us to be solemn all the time. He likes to hear us laff sometimes."

As time went on, Gracie went into films. Her best-known film was *Queen of Hearts*, in which she played and sang the story of her own life. Molesworth Street, Rochdale, Uncle Jimmy's Jollities, the Cosy Corner concert-party, some of Gracie's favourite songs and a bit of grand opera too – it was all there in *Queen of Hearts*. One homely touch which the film-makers

Gracie entertaining the men of a great shipyard – one of many such appearances during the second world war.

noticed: on Gracie's dressing-room table there was usually a jar of pickled cabbage, of which she was particularly fond! And for her lunch Gracie went, not to the stars' restaurant but down to the studio canteen, where all the electricians and carpenters went to eat.

It was said, at this time, that Gracie Fields was the highest paid film-star in the world, and that she was earning more money than even Greta Garbo. Did she enjoy her wealth? Well, as we shall see, she gave a good deal of it away, and was only too glad to be able to help her friends; but there were moments when she would sigh and say: "What I really want is a cottage in the country and ten shillings a week!"

There are many stories of Gracie's generosity: money never stayed long in her pocket if she saw that anybody – whether a friend or a stranger – was in trouble or need. One day she read in a newspaper that

a youth named Johnny Lucas, of Ilford, Essex, a greengrocer's boy, had lost his pony "Tommy". "Tommy" meant everything to him: the pony was his friend, his pet and his living. Gracie lost no time, but bought Johnny a new pony.

Then there was a young painter named Brian Desmond Hurst who came from Ireland with a great plan to make a film about Irish fisher-folk called *Riders of the Sea*. He had tried to get someone to put up the money to make the film, but he had failed. "Who wants to see a film about a lot of fishermen?" he was asked. "A film like that won't make any money." Gracie thought differently, however: whether it made money or not, she was sure it would be a beautiful film which everyone ought to see. So she gave him a few thousand pounds out of her own savings. The film was made, and was a success.

Nor did Gracie forget her own family (her heart was never very far away from Rochdale). Much as she loved the narrow street where she was born, she wanted to give her parents more comfort and rest in their old age, so she bought them a house at Peacehaven, on the Sussex coast, and, for fun, had it all fitted out like a luxury liner, with cabins and a captain's bridge and all. She also gave a helping hand to her brother Tommy, who became a comedian in his own right.

So well-loved was Gracie that all the great names of England wanted to meet her; and there was a famous occasion while making a film when she was visited on the "set" by no less a personage than Lord Hewart, the Lord Chief Justice of England. And when Gracie went to Brighton one day, she discovered that a pleasure steamer had been named after her, and so she took a trip in the good ship *Gracie Fields*.

But she was soon to go a much longer voyage in another ship – to South Africa, where many thousands of people who had heard of her and seen her films were eagerly waiting for her to appear in person. The whole Fields (or Stansfield) family came down to the docks at Southampton to see her off, for our Gracie had never been so far abroad before. Long before the ship had left Southampton, Gracie was saying to her family: "Ee, I'm fair homesick already and we haven't left England yet!"

The South Africans loved her so much that they waited for hours at wayside stations for her train to go through – and then made her get out and give a short concert on the platform! And she spent the warmest Christmas she ever remembered in Johannesburg.

After her return to England, a strange rumour was spread, saying that Gracie was going to retire. How wide of the mark this was we can see today, fifteen years later; but it would be typical of Gracie that, at the very height of her success, she should wonder whether she could keep it up, and go on giving her very best to her millions of friends. But the mood passed, and the Lancashire lass who earned £3 a minute made a new film, *The Show Goes On*, which again brought in incidents from her own life – especially the concert party on the sands at Colwyn Bay in which she made her début.

It was about this time (1936) that she bought the lovely villa on the Isle of Capri, in Italy, which is now her permanent home. But she still spent as much on others as on herself, and in this year she founded the famous Gracie Fields Orphanage at Peacehaven, where twenty motherless and fatherless children could grow up happily at her expense. "And I hope there'll be two hundred of them some day!" said Gracie. She found

time to look up her old friends at Rochdale, too, and to kick off for Rochdale Hornets Rugby Football Team.

Next year came the Coronation of King George VI – a year of great excitement all over England. For Gracie, in particular, it was a great and moving occasion, for Rochdale gave her the highest honour a town can confer upon one of its citizens: it made Gracie Fields a "Freeman of Rochdale", so that, by ancient tradition, she became the ever-welcome guest of the town who could do no wrong here! And as she rode through the streets in triumph on a fire-engine, she knew the happiness we all want to know, that of being popular among the people who mean most to us, the people of our own home-town. And haven't we all wanted to ride on a fire-engine ?

The King, too, had remembered Gracie in the Honours List. For Gracie is entitled to sign her name "Gracie Fields, C.B.E." – Commander of the British Empire, for outstanding services to her fellow-countrymen.

Gracie could not show her appreciation of her C.B.E. except by saying, "thank you, your Majesty", but she could return Rochdale's hospitality – and she did, on a big scale. She invited 9,000 Rochdale people to London for a party at Alexandra Palace, and took them to see Windsor Castle first.

Everybody knows that Gracie has made a lot of money in her hard-working lifetime, but many people forget how many times she has sung for nothing, to help a good cause or a deserving charity. Concerts in aid of Charing Cross Hospital, concerts for the prisoners at Pentonville, Poppy Day Crusades for the Earl Haig Fund for wounded soldiers – it is no wonder that General Sir Ian Hamilton once described her as "an angel with a heart of gold".

When Gracie went off to Hollywood to make more films, people wondered whether, like so many film-stars who leave England, she would be tempted to stay in the land of the dollar. Would the Americans "glamourise" her, and take away the natural simplicity for which we all love her ? Not a bit of it! One of the first people to befriend her in Hollywood was the great Charlie Chaplin, who had been on the English music-halls himself when Gracie was just starting her career. "What an artist she is!" he said. "And what a good friend!" In fact, Gracie admits that she was rather frightened of Hollywood, where everybody seemed so smart and lived in such luxury.

But she came back to us in the end – as brilliant as ever, and with a new song: "Wish me luck as you wave me goodbye", which has become as much a part of her as the famous "Sally".

FLICK – AND THE VANISHING NEW GIRL

WRITTEN BY GEORGE BEARDMORE   DRAWN BY AITCHISON

FELICITY ('FLICK' FOR SHORT) OF LOWER IV B AT ST. BRENDAN'S SCHOOL IS ONE NIGHT SETTLING HERSELF OFF TO SLEEP —

FELICITY, HERE'S YOUR NEW ROOM-MATE, HELENA

— WHEN THE LANGUAGE MISTRESS — MISS MILLER — BRINGS A STRANGER TO THE DORMITORY.

I LEFT A SWISS CONVENT TO COME HERE

YOU'LL LOVE ST. BRENDAN'S — IT'S SUPER

MY PARENTS THOUGHT ENGLAND WOULD BE SAFER.

GOODNESS!

YOU HAVE BEEN TRICKED INTO COMING TO ENGLAND. ENEMIES SURROUND YOU. BE OUTSIDE THE LODGE GATES AT MIDNIGHT AND I WILL HELP YOU. DESTROY THIS.

A FRIEND.

SO AT MIDNIGHT —

I WONDER WHOM I'LL FIND AT THE LODGE GATES!

WHILE MISS MILLER —

IS THAT YOU, JORG? THE TRICK'S WORKED. BRING THE CAR ROUND TO THE LODGE GATES AND BE READY TO JUMP ON HER

— AND IN THE DORMITORY ABOVE —

WHAT'S THE MATTER, FLICK?

THAT NEW GIRL'S RUNNING AWAY AND I'M GOING AFTER HER

IN CLASS NEXT DAY ~

WHAT'S GOING ON AT THE BACK THERE?

PLEASE, MISS, THE NEW GIRL'S FALLEN ASLEEP ~ AND SO HAS FELICITY!

BOTH OF YOU WILL WRITE OUT 200 TIMES "I MUST KEEP AWAKE IN CLASS"~

~AND, HELENA, YOU WILL COME TO SEE ME AT BREAK

AS RINGLEADER, HELENA, YOU WILL FORFEIT GAMES THIS AFTERNOON AND TAKE A NOTE FOR ME INTO THE VILLAGE

BUT THE HEAD PUT IT OUT OF BOUNDS FOR ME, MISS!

ARE YOU TRYING TO DEFY ME, GIRL? YOU WILL NOW WRITE OUT YOUR IMPOSITION 400 TIMES. DO AS I SAY

YES, MISS MILLER

THIS TIME I WILL SEE THAT JORG DOES NOT BUNGLE THINGS

AND THAT AFTERNOON ~

GOOD! THERE'S NO DOUBT THIS TIME THAT HE'S GOT HER ~

~AND I CAN BE SURE THAT THAT INTERFERING CHILD FELICITY ISN'T FOLLOWING HER

OH GOLLY, ~

~THERE'S HELENA BEEN KIDNAPPED BY THAT AWFUL MAN WHO JUMPED OUT ON ME LAST NIGHT

YOU'RE IN NEXT, FLICK

SHAN'T BE A MINUTE

And never till this day has Flick betrayed that the new girl was anything more than just—Helena.

MARTIN AITCHISON

THE STORY OF

Vivien Leigh

★ Told by Maud Miller with illustrations by Bill Dowsett ★

SHE was eight years old when she made the most important speech of her life – as it turned out.

"I am going to be an actress," she said.

When she made this little speech it was at boarding school, in reply to a visitor. She meant what she said.

This is where Vivien Leigh differs from most of us. She never lost sight of her ambition. Everything that happened to her contributed in some way to her development as an actress on the stage and in the cinema.

She was born in Darjeeling, within sight of Mount Everest. Her father, Mr Ernest Hartley, a business man, had his office, then, in Calcutta. During the hot seasons he sent his wife to the Himalaya Hills, and there on a fifth of November, Vivien made her 'world debut.'

Her earliest recollection is 'looking at Everest and Kinchinjanga and thinking how wonderful it must be, away up, so remote, looking down at the world spread out like a pale, flowered carpet, clear, and perfect . . . '

Perfect. Perfection. Words that belong peculiarly to Vivien, who applies the same standards of perfection to her job, and everything that goes with it.

Perfection in choice of the right frock for the right occasion, exquisite in line, colour and design, worn with the right accessories and jewellery, the correct artistic frame for her personality. Just the right perfume, the tailored shoes, and *one* splash of colour.

I once found her washing down the walls of her Chelsea home with great energy. In an outsize overall – borrowed from the housekeeper, and tied round the middle like a French porter's blue blouse, she looked like something Dior had just dreamed up.

Vivien was very lucky in having the right parents for her kind of personality, happy people who wanted her to have fun, too.

Mr Hartley had done a good deal of amateur dramatics in Calcutta, where there was no English theatre, and if you wanted that kind of entertainment, you had to make it for yourself . . . experience that came in very handy when it came to entertaining his small daughter.

As bedtime attractions Mrs Hartley provided a wide choice of reading . . . Kipling, and Hans Andersen, Bible stories, Charles Kingsley and the simpler Greek mythology.

In such a setting Vivien, earlier than most children, acquired the sense of social serenity that became one of her greatest charms.

For her own amusement, among all those grown-ups she started her own hobby . . . a hobby with the fascinating name of 'serendipity'. The dictionary describes this as 'the faculty of making happy and interesting discoveries by accident', taken from the fairy-tale 'The Three Princes of Serendip', an ancient name for Ceylon.

Years later, when she reached the importance of having her name and biography in *Who's Who in the Theatre*, she listed 'serendipity and arranging flowers', as her recreations.

In schooldays, however, there was little time for serendipity. Her studies were centred round her ambition. Extra tuition in elocution, voice production, deportment, ballet, the study of Shakespeare, Sheridan, Trollope, Scott and Dickens . . . they were all in her curriculum.

Taking it by and large Vivien was a very normal child, more sensitive than some, perhaps, with a quick sympathy of her own for anything that was hurt . . . a bird with a broken wing, or the sight of a child smaller than herself that looked unhappy.

She *adored* going to the theatre. She still does. Anyone who took her out from school found themselves inveigled into taking her to the theatre.

O NE of her greatest thrills – she was thirteen at the time – was being taken to Stratford-on-Avon to see *Hamlet*. Ever afterwards a green spotlight in any theatre, anywhere, gave her lovely shivers in her spine, and the joyful anticipation that a ghost might creep out of the wings . . .

Her parents came home from India. They decided to spend a few years enjoying life in Britain and on the Continent.

Vivien was with them some of the time, but most of the time she was at school. In Italy, for a year. Then in Paris.

Here she studied drama with an actress from the Comédie Française. She acquired a good French accent, was taken to the Louvre and other galleries to study painting and sculpture, to the theatre and the ballet, and all the other subjects that are considered fitting at a smart finishing school.

She spent a year in Bavaria, where she learnt to speak German with the right accent. She was not far from Salzburg, which meant music and Festivals. She absorbed it all, like an enthusiastic human sponge.

In Bavaria, too, she also acquired much of her knowledge of cookery. She not only likes good food, but she likes to know how it is done. For a time her favourite bedside literature was a cookery book.

Schooldays over, she went to her mother's home in Ireland, where she spent a few months doing all the things that made up the life of a débutante just emerging from her schoolgirl chrysalis.

But all this was a marking-time period for her.

She wanted to be an actress . . . remember?

So . . . in the nicest possible way, she suggested to her parents that she should be doing something constructive about her career, and could she please go to the Royal Academy of Dramatic Art instead of another season of huntin', shootin' and fishin', and dancing?

While she was studying at R.A.D.A. where her classmates included Rachel Kempson, Leueen MacGrath, and Dorothy Hyson, she met a man whose Christian name was 'Leigh'.

They were married very shortly, a fact that depressed the R.A.D.A. Principal, Sir Kenneth Barnes. Her work had impressed him, and it so often happened when a

Vivien Leigh in her sensationally successful portrayal of Scarlett O'Hara.

promising pupil got married, her career as an actress would be thrown overboard.

Vivien surprised him by returning to the Academy a year or two after her marriage. She had a baby daughter, Suzanne, she had an excellent nanny, a perfect domestic staff to run the house, and she *wanted* to continue her drama studies.

One day at R.A.D.A. a fellow student, Hazel Terry, talked to her about films, and suggested it might be 'rather fun and good experience' to do some work as 'extras'.

They set out together to try their luck.

Their luck was in. They got jobs in *Things Are Looking Up*, a Cicely Courtneidge film, at a guinea a day.

On location in the country for exteriors – the place was Chobham, in Surrey. Vivien persuaded an assistant director that she wanted to be an actress, and could she have some lines of dialogue, please? Just like that!

She got her dialogue, and returned from the location by car, with the 'special girls', instead of with the mob in the coach provided for the extras!

The Vivien Leigh determination had begun to take root.

Now the roots began to grow, firmly and strongly.

On one occasion at least, she distinguished herself by turning down an offer from Ivor Novello, to play a small

There was someone else, too, who saw the 'spark'. Sydney Carroll, producer and critic, who gave her the break in the play he was then producing, *The Mask of Virtue*.

After the first performance Vivien did not go to bed at all that night . . . she waited up to see what the newspaper critics had to say about her, mainly because she felt very critical of her own performance!

All that day telephones rang, reporters and photographers stormed her home, and Alexander Korda offered her an important film contract.

She had to wait nearly two years before her first film for Korda, *Fire Over England*, because Korda was then

Notley Abbey–the Oliviers' much loved country home.

part in a play called *Murder in Mayfair*. The salary mentioned was £4 a week.

"I can get thirty shillings a day in films," she told him.

"Fine . . ." said Novello. "Go ahead and get your thirty bob . . . and good luck!"

Soon after this, she really made news, in *The Mask of Virtue*, her second stage play.

This was the play that established her, as a young actress to watch, and which led to her first big adventure in films.

Gracie Fields also had a share in her success. Playing a small part in one of Gracie's films, *Look up and Laugh*, Vivien was not doing very well, for all she was trying her hardest. She just could not get the effects the director wanted. Then she overheard someone on the set say she'd never be any good in pictures because her neck was too long! She was very depressed.

"Eh, luv," said Gracie. "Don't cry! . . . You'll get over it all right . . . you see, you've *got* something, and you'll be all right . . . now come and have a cupper wi' me in the canteen . . ."

building the Denham studios, so she continued her work in the theatre.

Fire Over England was a story of the Elizabethan days of adventure, of sailing ships and empire building. Flora Robson was Queen Elizabeth, Vivien her lady-in-waiting. There was a 'fictional' hero, called Michael Ingoldsby, who fell in love with the lady-in-waiting. His name was Laurence Olivier.

Later Vivien worked for a time with the Oxford University Dramatic Society. She appeared as Ann Boleyn in *Henry VIII* at the Open Air Theatre in Regent's Park. She went to Denmark as 'guest artiste', with the Old Vic Company, at the personal invitation of the late Lilian Baylis, to play Ophelia to Olivier's Hamlet in the original Shakespeare setting at Elsinore.

The story goes that Vivien had seen the Old Vic production of *Hamlet* 14 times, but her performance at rehearsals drew some fiery criticism from producer Tyrone Guthrie.

He thought her acting was really quite good and he

recognised the determination in her. *His* problem was her voice, which was not very strong. All right in a small theatre, but he was afraid she might not be able to 'throw it round' the wide open spaces at Elsinore.

When the time came, however, the Guthrie teaching technique paid high dividends and both Vivien and the company were a great success.

Had she never made another film, nor appeared ever again on the stage, *Gone With the Wind*, alone would justify that childhood assertion "I am going to be an actress."

It was one of the longest, biggest, most expensive, most spectacular films ever made! It was in colour. The 'City of Atlanta' set was the largest ever built till then, and contained 7,000 feet of streets. Vivien had 40 changes of costume.

Vivien had been fascinated by the character of Scarlett from the day she began reading Margaret Mitchell's 1,037-page novel of the Civil War days in Georgia.

She brooded over Scarlett for months. "I believe I could play Scarlett," she told me once, while she was filming *A Yank at Oxford*.

Characteristically Vivien did not go after the role of Scarlett like a bull at a gate. She did the jobs that were nearest, in films and in the theatre.

Then luck, circumstance and romance brought the whole thing into sharp focus. If Vivien prodded the luck with the steel shaft of her determination that is entirely her own affair!

SHE was slated to appear at the Old Vic, in *A Midsummer Night's Dream*. She had a few weeks' leisure before rehearsals were due to begin. She had a lot of friends in America, including Laurence Olivier, who was then making *Wuthering Heights* in Hollywood. She flew to America.

When Vivien arrived in Hollywood they were burning up a lot of old sets, to represent the burning of Atlanta, and producer Selznick had not yet cast his leading lady.

He had tested nearly two hundred 'possibles' and interviewed several thousand more for two years, without finding the right girl.

On the very night she reached Hollywood Selznick's brother Myron, took Vivien along to see the fire . . . which was then engaging half the fire brigades in the district to keep it under control.

During an interval in the proceedings Myron drew his brother on one side, to introduce Vivien.

"Here's your Scarlett," he said without any particular emphasis. He knew his brother.

Vivien made three 'tests' in one day, of various stages of Scarlett's career.

Then she went off on a motor tour of California.

About 130 miles N.N.E. of Hollywood the Selznick Organisation caught up with her.

"You're Scarlett . . ." she was told by a breathless and hatless young man, whose drop-head coupé had driven across her path and stopped her.

"At least we think you are . . . will you please come back and make just one more test?"

Vivien went back, made the final test, was cast as Scarlett, became overnight headline news in the papers . . . and for the next six months lived, dreamed, thought, acted Scarlett O'Hara.

She was awarded her first Oscar for her performance in *Gone With the Wind*.

In terms of time it was less than five years after her first stage triumph in *The Mask of Virtue*, and just a little over five years since the day she got her first 'extra' role in *Things Are Looking Up*.

THE World War was crowding the newspaper columns when the film was first shown – but for a long time there was always a little bit of space for some item of news about it, or its stars.

A few months later Vivien created another record. The girl who had been nothing but a name to American audiences suddenly became visible in six places at once, in New York.

Cashing in on her success as Scarlett, the cinemas rushed to show some of her earlier films. She was also appearing on the stage in *Romeo and Juliet* with Laurence Olivier.

In the story of Vivien Leigh the Oscar she won for Scarlett signified her graduation as an actress. Those of us who knew her well were not surprised. The others who had to be convinced were not only convinced, but amazed.

Of her own performance Vivien remained critical. Ten years later she told me: "I wish I could have played Scarlett *now*, with greater experience. I could have made a much better job of her."

That . . . from the girl who had just won another Oscar, for her Blanche, in *A Streetcar Named Desire!*

There were many awards handed out for G.W.T.W. and for Vivien, as an actress, but her life as a private citizen at that time was also rather important to her, for she became the wife of Olivier just before they began the tour in America of *Romeo and Juliet*.

Vivien was not good as Juliet. She makes no bones about it. I do not think she will mind if I tell you what she told me not long ago, when I was writing an article about her for a magazine.

"I think you should mention my flop," she said, and just to make sure I would remember, she pencilled a note on the rough draft of the article!

With Olivier she made *Lady Hamilton*, a sugar-coated version of the Nelson story, that had an historical parallel with the chapter of British history we were then fighting.

Our wartime Prime Minister, Winston Churchill, saw *Lady Hamilton* thirteen times, and wept with emotion at every single one of them!

The Oliviers came home from America when the blitz was in full spate. Then she appeared on the stage in *The Doctor's Dilemma*, while her husband was serving with the Fleet Air Arm.

While Olivier was filming *Henry V* she went overseas to the Western desert, on an *Ensa* tour, with Beatrice Lillie, Leslie Henson and Dorothy Dickson.

On her return home she made the film *Caesar and Cleopatra*.

For Vivien, this was rather an unhappy experience. The illness that sent her into nine months' retirement later on, was beginning. She wanted to make a good job of Shaw's young Cleopatra – but she so hated the time spent at Denham making the film, that she did not see it on the screen for five years.

And that was only because she wanted to study hair-styles, costumes and decor for the Festival of Britain theatre season, when she played Cleopatra on the stage, with Olivier, in Shaw's *Caesar and Cleopatra*, and Shakespeare's *Antony and Cleopatra*.

The driving force that stimulates any good actress kept Vivien going while she acted *The Skin of our Teeth* on the London stage . . . but there came a time when the doctors said STOP, and packed her off to rest, after a spell in hospital.

She was like an overworked motor-car. She was not only run-down, but, like the engine and the tyres, worn out too.

So while the 'engineers' got busy renewing her, she rested in dry dock . . . to be reconditioned,

regeared and returned ready for the road again!

This was the time she first grew to love Notley Abbey, her first real home for many years. She had not cared very much for it when Olivier took her down to see it. It was derelict, badly in need of modernising – but it had possibilities.

Built in the thirteenth century, a place of grey stone, mullioned windows and draughts, it was not Vivien's idea of comfort. Gradually they had reshaped it, made it into a home, with a profitable farm attached.

As she grew stronger Vivien discovered gardening – she had always loved flowers, now she could plant the seeds, and watch them grow.

Notley gave her back health, and strength for a long season at the Old Vic, and for a strenuous tour in Australia . . . 'tiring but fascinating' is how she described it. "We spent so much time travelling, we had no time to get to know people."

She likes people and once you are a friend, you are there, in her warm friendship, for life. She has had the same secretary for years. When she makes a film in Hollywood, the secretary and the hairdresser she had while making *Gone with the Wind* leave their husbands and families to look after themselves while they look after Vivien. She has had the same domestic staff for years. She loves jewels for their lustre and their sheen, and for their sentimental value. When thieves burgled Notley Abbey while she was recuperating from that breakdown which sent her back to bed for another three months in 1953, it was not the mink and jewellery they took that upset her. It was just one ring, of no very great value. Olivier gave it to her, to mark a particular incident in both their lives, and as such she valued it more than anything else.

It was, perhaps, fortunate for her peace of mind that when she was ill; then, she was too ill to know anything about the publicity that her breakdown evoked.

She would have hated it. The only kind of publicity that interests her is a piece of constructive criticism about her work . . .

She still says: "I just want to be a good actress."

SUMUNA'S SOUTH SEA ISLE

Story by TERRY STANFORD
Drawn by NEVIN

YES, LITTLE ONE, SUMUNA ALSO SEES THE SMALL SHIP IN THE LAGOON—AND ITS BRIGHT HAIRED STRANGER.

SQUAWK! SQUAWK! SQUA-AWK!

CHIRRUK! CHIRRUK! WE-EEK!

SUMUNA MUST SEE WHO THIS STRANGER IS — AND WHAT HE IS DOING HERE!

WHAT A STRANGE-LOOKING BOAT! WHO CAN THE OWNER BE? SUMUNA WILL SWIM OUT AND SEE. WAIT HERE, BIG BEAK.

I WILL CLIMB THAT LITTLE LADDER AND SEE WHO IS ON THE BOAT.

SEE, MASTER! GIRL!

IT'S A GIRL, ALL RIGHT, LOKI! THE QUESTION IS WHAT DOES SHE WANT WITH US?

NO! NO! SUMUNA GO AWAY QUIETLY! SUMUNA ONLY WANT TO SEE BOAT.

DON'T BE SILLY! WE'RE NOT GOING TO HURT YOU!

MASTER GOOD, ME GOOD. YOU O.K!

I'M TIM O'HARA, A ONE-MAN PEARLING OUTFIT. LOKI'S MY DIVER. I COULD USE YOUR HELP.

PEARL-FISHERS ARE BAD MEN. LONG AGO KILL FATHER, MOTHER, ALL. SUMUNA WILL NOT HELP YOU!

WE'RE NOT ALL LIKE THAT, SUMUNA. I'VE A VERY DIFFERENT REASON FOR SEEKING PEARLS.

PEARLS MEAN TROUBLE— AND BLOOD. SUMUNA KNOWS. MONEY IS ONLY REASON. THERE IS NO OTHER.

MY FATHER WAS A PEARL-FISHER, SUMUNA. HE DISAPPEARED, PEARLS, BOAT, EVERYTHING. I NEED MONEY TO PAY BACK THE MEN WHO FINANCED HIS EXPEDITION AND NOW BRAND HIM A THIEF AND A CHEAT. THAT'S WHY I'M A PEARL-FISHER. IT ALSO GIVES ME AN OPPORTUNITY TO SEARCH FOR A CERTAIN CAP'N ERICKSON, WHO WAS ONCE MY FATHER'S PARTNER — AND WHO I THINK KNOWS PLENTY ABOUT MY FATHER'S DISAPPEARANCE.

SUMUNA IS SORRY. SHE WAS WRONG. SUMUNA WILL SHOW YOU WHERE PEARLS ARE.

THAT'S GREAT SUMUNA! AND I'LL TAKE NO MORE THAN I NEED TO PAY MY FATHER'S DEBT.

FIRST GET FRESH WATER, AND FRUIT, HEY, MASTER?

ON THE OTHER SIDE OF THE LAGOON

WHAT'S YOUNG O'HARA REALLY LOOKING FOR, PEARLS — OR US? EH, SACHEZ?

YOU THEENK HE KNOW YOU KEEL HEES FATHER, STEAL HEES PEARL, SCUTTLE HEES BOAT, NO?

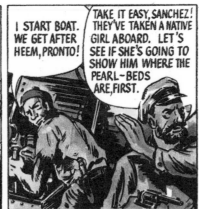

ONE HOUR LATER. SUMUNA TELLS TIM TO STOP THE BOAT.

SO THE OYSTER BEDS ARE DOWN THERE, EH?

YES, TIM, THIS IS THE PLACE. YOU WILL SEE.

RIGHT! LOKI, YOU GO DOWN AND HAVE A LOOK-SEE.

YES, MASTER. I GO NOW!

HOW IS IT DOWN THERE, LOKI?

OYSTER BIG AS PLATE, MASTER.. PLENTY. EVERYWHERE YOU LOOK.

YOU SEE, TIM? SUMUNA DOES NOT TELL YOU STORIES!

I CAN HARDLY WAIT TO GET DOWN THERE! YOU STAND BY AND WORK THE WINCH, LOKI. O.K?

YES, MASTER. YOU LEAVE WINCH TO LOKI.

HOW DOES HE COME UP AGAIN, LOKI?

EASY, MISSY. HIM GIVE THREE TUG ON ROPE, LOKI HAUL-M UP BY WINCH.

SOME TIME LATER!

MASTER DOWN LONG TIME, LOKI HOPE NOTHING GONE WRONG DOWN THERE.

DO NOT WORRY, LOKI. SOON HE WILL PULL ON THE ROPE.

FOUR TUGS! TIM IS IN TROUBLE. WHAT SHALL WE DO?

DON'T YOU WORRY, MISSY. LOKI HIM GO DOWN, DOUBLE — QUICK!

LOKI DIVES DOWN AND FINDS TIM ON THE SEA-BED.

HE SEES THAT TIM HAS CAUGHT HIS FOOT IN THE SHELL OF A GIANT CLAM.

HE TRIES TO PULL TIM LOOSE... BUT THE CLAM'S GRIP IS TOO TIGHT.

LOKI CAN DO NOTHING MORE BUT RETURN TO THE SURFACE...

GIANT—CLAM—GOT—MASTER—BY—FOOT. HIM—TRAPPED!

A GIANT CLAM? SUMUNA WILL FIX HIM. YOU, WATCH!

MISSY SAVE MASTER? LOKI NOT UNDERSTAND.

SUMUNA DIVES DOWNWARDS TO WHERE TIM IS STILL IN THE GRIP OF THE GIANT CLAM.

USING HER KNIFE SHE CUTS OFF SEAWEED . . . .

SHE WAVES THIS IN FRONT OF THE CLOSED JAWS OF THE CLAM...

SWISH! SWISH!

SLOWLY THE CLAM'S JAWS OPEN RELEASING TIM WHO BY THIS TIME IS EXHAUSTED.

SUMUNA SIGNALS TO LOKI ABOVE TO WIND UP THE WINCH...

AND TOGETHER TIM AND SUMUNA RISE SLOWLY TO THE SURFACE.

YOU SAVE MASTER! BLESS YOU, MISSY!

GET HIM ABOARD QUICK, LOKI. HE HAS THE CRAMPS. HE MAY DIE!

QUICK, MISSY! GOT TO HURRY!

THAT IS THE LAST STRAP!

OUCH! GO EASY, THERE!

OH, HE IS ALL RIGHT! THAT IS WONDERFUL!

PHEW! LOKI HIM NEAR LAST GASP, TOO!

Tim descends again to the sea bed and fills basket after basket with the huge oysters. Loki and Sumuna are so intent on keeping guard over their friend they do not see the approach of the black lugger from the other side. After a huge haul Tim surfaces to safety again.

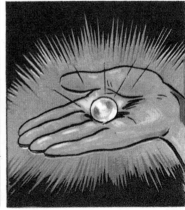

WE'RE COOKED, SANCHEZ. THE BULLETS JUST BOUNCE OFF HIM!

NO, NO, NO! SAVE ME, CAPITAINE!

QUESTION IS, WILL THAT SETTLE OUR SAVAGE FRIEND OR WILL HE COME AFTER US?

TIM-LOOK!

THAT'S SETTLED THE END OF THE MANTA. I SHOULDN'T LOOK SUMUNA IF I WERE YOU.

NO, TIM, I CANNOT— EVEN IF THE MEN WERE WICKED AND THE MANTA WAS A MONSTER.

BAD AS THEY WERE WE CANNOT LEAVE THEM HERE TO THEIR FATE. CAN YOU SEE ANY SIGN OF THEM LOKI?

LOOK, BOSS! BAD MEN HANG ON TO WRECKAGE.

Now that Erickson and Sanchez have lost the power their machine gun gave them, they are in the hands of Tim who decides to take them back to the mainland, where the officials can see that justice is done.

BACK AT SUMUNA'S ISLAND ONCE MORE.

THIS PEARL WILL FETCH FAR MORE THAN I SHALL EVER NEED, SUMUNA. COME BACK TO ENGLAND WITH US. YOU'D LIKE IT, THERE, I KNOW.

NO, TIM. SUMUNA BELONGS ON HER ISLAND AND YOU TO THE BIG WORLD BEYOND THE HORIZON. LET US EACH STAY WHERE WE TRULY BELONG.

SUMUNA'S RIGHT, LOKI, ONLY SOMEHOW I WISH IT DIDN'T HAVE TO END THIS WAY.

GOOD-BYE, SUMUNA. I'LL BE COMING BACK ONE DAY.

GOOD-BYE, TIM. SUMUNA WILL BE WAITING!

THE END

Margot Fonteyn

Leonide Massine

Alicia Markova

Moira Shearer

"Swan Lake"
Margot Fonteyn & Robert Helpmann

"The Sleeping Beauty"
Moira Shearer & Michael Somes

"Don Quichotte"
Sally Gilmour & John Field

Anna Pavlova, the world's most famous ballerina.

Margot Fonteyn as she appears in *Le Lac des Cygnes*.

Belle of the Ballet
IN Little MISS NOBODY

STORY BY GEORGE BEARDMORE : DRAWN BY JOHN WORSLEY

BELLE AUBURN AND HER FRIENDS MAMIE AND DAVID, PUPILS AT THE ARÉNSKA SCHOOL OF BALLET, HAVE DISCOVERED A MYSTERY. LATE ONE AFTERNOON IN THE SCHOOL'S ATTIC...

MAMIE, DAVID — SHE'S THERE AGAIN!

WHAT'S SHE DOING NOW, BELLE? — ARABESQUES, I THINK.

CLIMB UP AND HAVE A LOOK. — GOSH, THIS TABLE'S A BIT WEAK AT THE KNEES!

THERE — DID YOU SEE HER? — YOU'RE RIGHT, BELLE. SHE'S DOING ARABESQUES.

AND WE WERE DOING ARABESQUES THIS MORNING. EVERYTHING WE DO SHE REPEATS ABOUT THIS TIME EVERY AFTERNOON.

THE MYSTERY LIES ACROSS THE STREET FROM THE ARENSKA SCHOOL IN A TOP FLOOR ROOM WHERE A GIRL IS DANCING. THAT'S ALL WE EVER SEE OF HER — JUST LEGS AND NO BODY. POOR LITTLE MISS NOBODY!

NOW WHAT'S HAPPENING — LOOK! SHE'S STOPPED DANCING. SOMEBODY'S JUST COME IN.

—IT'S A MAN! AND HE'S SHAKING HIS FIST AT US. WHATEVER FOR? HERE, STOP DITHERING! — I'M NOT DITHERING. THE TABLE'S GIV—

WHOOSH! OH, HELP!

ONCE INSIDE THE SCHOOL . . .

SSSH! NOT A WHISPER.

I'LL DO THE GRAMOPHONE.

AND I THE HOUSE-LIGHTS.

AND THEN WE'LL ALL SPRING INTO POSITION. READY?

MEANWHILE, IN THE KITCHEN

BUT 'OW CAN YOU SAY BALLET IS A WASTE OF TIME EEF YOU NEVAIR SEE IT?

MADAM, I *KNOW* — AND I WILL NOT HAVE MY LITTLE GIRL IMITATE A PACK OF HOOLIGANS!

SSSH! WHAT EES THAT MUSIC?

AND THIS IS BELLE'S SURPRISE—*SWAN LAKE* AS IT WAS TO BE DANCED FOR MADAME ARENSKA'S BIRTHDAY.

HERE THEY ARE, FOLKS.

PITY WE COULDN'T CHANGE.

GOOD GRACIOUS, WHAT'S THIS?

THIS, MY FRIEND, IS BALLET— SOMETHING YOU NEVER SEE BEFORE.

BUT IT'S FASCINATING — ENCHANTING! AND TO THINK I'VE STOPPED MY LITTLE GIRL . . .

SO NOW YOU LET 'ER DANCE, EH?

SOME MINUTES LATER

OF COURSE SHE SHALL DANCE. SHE MUST COME HERE FOR LESSONS.

AND MADAME ARENSKA SHALL TURN HER INTO LITTLE MISS SOMEBODY!

THE END

JENNY LOVELACE
AND
THE HAUNTED TOWER

A.D. 1657. TROUBLESOME TIMES FOR SUPPORTERS OF THE EXILED KING CHARLES II. BAD NEWS IS FAST APPROACHING THE HOME OF THE RENOWNED CAVALIER — COLONEL HARRY LOVELACE AND HIS DAUGHTER, JENNY.

COLONEL LOVELACE! THE ROUNDHEADS ARE ON THEIR WAY TO ARREST YOU!

THE ROUNDHEADS! HOW SOON WILL THEY BE HERE?

YOU HAVE LESS THAN AN HOUR. I MUST RIDE TO WARN OTHERS. GOD SAVE THE KING!

QUICK JENNY! TO THE STABLES. WE MUST FLEE

SHALL WE TO FRANCE AND JOIN THE KING?

I SHALL JOIN THE KING. BUT FOR YOU THE JOURNEY IS TOO DANGEROUS. YOU WILL GO TO YOUR UNCLE— SIR JOHN HOWARD

PLEASE LET ME COME TO FRANCE, FATHER. THOUGH I'M A GIRL I CAN STILL FIGHT AND SERVE THE KING

NO, JENNY! I INSIST THAT YOU REMAIN UNDER THE PROTECTION OF YOUR UNCLE

THE ROUNDHEAD TROOPS ARRIVE. JENNY AND HER FATHER HAVE ESCAPED JUST IN TIME

SURROUND THE HOUSE!

WE'RE TOO LATE! THE ROYALIST DOGS HAVE ESCAPED! BURN THE HOUSE DOWN!

OH — THE BEASTS! THEY'RE BURNING DOWN OUR HOME!

GIVE THANKS WE STILL HAVE OUR LIVES. COME — WE MUST RIDE HARD TO SIR JOHN.

THAT EVENING. THE TWO FUGITIVES APPROACH MEDLEY CHASE, IN SOMERSET — THE HOME OF JENNY'S UNCLE, SIR JOHN HOWARD

SIR JOHN HOWARD AND SILAS QUINN HIS BUTLER ARE IN THE LIBRARY

SIR JOHN, THOUGH CRIPPLED BY AN OLD WOUND, STILL SERVES KING CHARLES — BY GUILE!

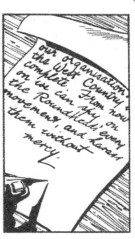

our organisation, the West Country, complete. From now on we can try the Roundheads, every movement, and harass them without mercy.

YOU HAVE VISITORS, SIR JOHN. IT IS COLONEL LOVELACE AND HIS DAUGHTER

MY BROTHER — AND JENNY? I HOPE NOTHING IS AMISS. QUICKLY — GO AND ADMIT THEM.

LOOK, FATHER, THAT RUINED TOWER OVER THERE! DOESN'T IT LOOK MYSTERIOUS?

WELCOME TO MEDLEY CHASE! SIR JOHN IS IN THE LIBRARY.

JOHN — WE NEED YOUR HELP.

HARRY! JENNY! WHAT BRINGS YOU HERE SO UNEXPECTEDLY?

QUINN — FETCH FOOD FOR MY GUESTS. NOW, HARRY, WHAT'S AMISS?

... AND THEN THEY BURNT OUR HOUSE. OH! I WISH I WERE A MAN THAT I COULD FIGHT THEM

I KNOW, MY DEAR — I REGRET MY CRIPPLED STATE FOR THE SAME REASON

THEN IT'S AGREED — I'LL TO FRANCE AND JENNY MUST BIDE WITH YOU

YES, YOU MUST LEAVE AT ONCE, HARRY

A SAD TALE THEY TELL...

MEANWHILE THERE ARE STRANGE HAPPENINGS NEAR THE MYSTERIOUS TOWER. TWO VILLAGERS WATCH IN TERROR

SEE — THERE 'TIS AGAIN!

LORD SAVE US ALL

THE GHOST!

'TIS THE HORSEMAN'!

UNAWARE OF THE HAPPENINGS AT THE TOWER, JENNY AND SIR JOHN HELP THE COLONEL TO PREPARE FOR HIS LONG JOURNEY

A FRESH HORSE FOR THE COLONEL

I'LL PACK SOME FOOD, FATHER

GOD SPEED, HARRY — HAVE CARE

WHEN I RETURN, IT WILL BE WITH THE KING'S ARMY. FAREWELL JENNY — KEEP COURAGE — REMEMBER YOU ARE THE DAUGHTER OF A CAVALIER

THE KING! IF ONLY I COULD FIND A WAY TO SERVE HIM.

A LIGHT! THERE'S A LIGHT IN THE TOWER!

A LIGHT, MISS JENNY? YOU ARE MISTAKEN

WHY, — IT'S GONE!

THERE'S SOMETHING VERY STRANGE GOING ON. I SWEAR I SAW A LIGHT

NEXT DAY, JENNY DECIDES TO EXPLORE HER NEW SURROUNDINGS

WHAT A LOVELY DAY. I SHALL GO FOR A RIDE.

OH — HE'S BEAUTIFUL. WE SHALL HAVE A WONDERFUL RIDE.

HE'S A FAVOURITE OF SIR JOHN'S, MISS JENNY

THE MYSTERIOUS TOWER. I MUST GO AND EXPLORE

THERE MUST BE A MAGNIFICENT VIEW FROM THE TOP. THERE'S THE DOOR I'LL SEE...

OH DEAR — IT'S LOCKED. I WONDER...

BUT WHAT'S THAT?

A FOOTPRINT!! SOMEONE ELSE HAS BEEN HERE!

OOH!

YOU FRIGHTENED ME — I DID NOT HEAR YOU

I FOLLOWED TO ENSURE YOUR SAFETY — 'TIS SAID THE TOWER IS HAUNTED

HAUNTED BY A GHOSTLY HORSEMAN, AND ALL WHO SEE HIM — DIE!

NONSENSE! — 'TIS AN OLD WIVES' TALE

I WONDER HOW QUINN KNEW I WAS AT THE TOWER

THAT NIGHT.... A MYSTERIOUS VISITOR...

ARRIVES AT MEDLEY CHASE

WHO CAN IT BE — AT THIS TIME OF NIGHT?

A CAVALIER! UNCLE JOHN MAY NEED ME. I'LL GO DOWN

THERE'S SOMEONE IN THE HALL!

QUINN! HE'S EAVESDROPPING

YOU RANG, SIR JOHN?

YES, ORDER MY CARRIAGE AT ONCE. AH, JENNY...

...I'M GLAD YOU ARE HERE. THIS IS M'SIEU JACOBY FROM FRANCE

ENCHANTE, M'MSELLE

M'SIEU — UNCLE, I MUST SPEAK TO YOU ABOUT...

NOT NOW, M'DEAR. I AM LEAVING AT ONCE TO BRING AN ESCORT OF OUR FRIENDS FOR M'SIEU

WATCH OVER M. JACOBY — HIS LIFE IS VERY PRECIOUS TO US. I'LL BE BACK SOON

LATER THAT NIGHT

CREAK! CREAK!!

WHAT WAS THAT?

QUINN! — I'LL GET MY CLOAK AND FOLLOW HIM

HE'S MAKING FOR THE HAUNTED TOWER!

SOMEONE ELSE IS ALSO MAKING FOR THE TOWER.

THE HORSEMAN — QUINN! OH! — — — THEY'VE DISAPPEARED!

I'LL TRY THE DOOR

IT'S STILL LOCKED — BUT I HEAR VOICES

JENNY STARTS TO EXPLORE WHEN SUDDENLY...

IF ONLY I COULD HEAR... PERHAPS THERE'S A WINDOW...

OOOOOOH!

A SECRET ENTRANCE!

STEPS! THEY MUST LEAD SOME-WHERE...

AND AT THE TOP OF THE STONE STAIRWAY, JENNY FINDS A SECRET DOOR INTO THE TURRET ROOM

SOMEONE'S IN THERE!

JENNY PEERS CAUTIOUSLY THROUGH THE DOOR

GUNPOWD[ER]

QUINN! A ROUNDHEAD SPY! AND THE TOWER'S A SECRET ARSENAL!

SIR JOHN WILL BE BACK WITH THE ROYALIST TROOPS WITHIN THE HOUR

GOOD ~ WE WILL ATTACK AT MIDNIGHT AND CAPTURE THEM ALL ~ INCLUDING M. JACOBY!

HOW WILL THE MEN KNOW WHEN TO ATTACK?

BY MY SIGNALS FROM THIS TURRET. THE FLASHING LIGHT MEANS "ATTACK" A STEADY LIGHT MEANS "WITHDRAW"

I MUST WARN M. JACOBY.

AS JENNY RUNS TO MEDLEY CHASE, A MOUNTED FIGURE LEAVES THE TOWER

THE HORSEMAN ~ A ROUNDHEAD OFFICER!

M'SIEU ~ I MUST WARN YOU. QUINN THE BUTLER IS A ROUNDHEAD SPY

M'MSELLE?

THERE IS A PLOT TO ATTACK AND CAPTURE US WHEN MY UNCLE RETURNS

JE NE COMPRENDS PAS M'MSELLE

OH, IF ONLY SIR JOHN WOULD HURRY HOME. SSH! THERE'S SOMEONE AT THE DOOR

BUT THE FRENCHMAN DOES NOT UNDERSTAND

THERE IS NOTHING YOU REQUIRE? THEN I SHALL RETIRE. GOODNIGHT, MISS JENNY

MEANWHILE SIR JOHN AND HIS FRIENDS, RACING BACK TO MEDLEY CHASE...

...MEET WITH TROUBLE OF A DIFFERENT KIND.

...AND ARE DELAYED

AT MEDLEY CHASE, JENNY IS ANXIOUSLY WAITING

IT IS ONLY A FEW MINUTES TO MIDNIGHT. SHOULD THE ROUNDHEADS ATTACK, M. JACOBY WILL BE IN DEADLY PERIL!

I MUST GET TO THE TOWER FIRST AND GIVE THE SIGNAL FOR THE ROUNDHEADS TO WITHDRAW

I MUST GET THERE BEFORE QUINN!

JENNY REACHES THE TOWER...

...GAINS THE TURRET ROOM...

...AND LIGHTS THE SIGNAL WHICH SHE HOPES WILL DISPERSE THE ROUNDHEAD TROOPS.

SHE IS NOT A MOMENT TOO SOON

FASTER, MAN — WE ARE BETRAYED!

QUICK — TO THE TURRET AND CHANGE THE SIGNAL

QUINN! AND THE ROUNDHEAD OFFICER! I MUST ESCAPE

THE SECRET DOOR!

SLAM!

THE DRAUGHT'S CLOSED IT. THEY'RE COMING UP. I'M TRAPPED!

PERHAPS I CAN BLOCK THE DOOR WITH A MUSKET

OOH — THE LAMP!

IT'S GIVING WAY...

BUT AT THAT MOMENT HELP ARRIVES FOR JENNY

QUICK JENNY, THROUGH THE SECRET DOOR

THE STORY OF MARIE CURIE

MARIE SLODOWSKA WAS THE YOUNGEST OF FIVE IN THE FAMILY OF A WARSAW PROFESSOR IN 1869. THEY WERE VERY POOR, LITTLE MARIE WAS A CLEVER CHILD.

HER MOTHER DIED WHEN SHE WAS 11 AND MARIE HELPED THE FAMILY INCOME BY TAKING PUPILS, BUT HER AMBITION WAS TO BECOME A SCIENTIST.

LATER SHE APPLIED TO THE UNIVERSITY OF CRACOW TO BECOME A SCIENCE STUDENT. THE PRINCIPAL THOUGHT IT A HUGE JOKE.

MARIE SAVED ENOUGH FROM HER TEACHING TO GO TO PARIS. THERE, IN A MISERABLE ATTIC, SHE STUDIED AND PASSED HER DEGREES IN MATHS AND PHYSICS.

IN PARIS SHE MET PIERRE CURIE, A SCIENTIST WHO WAS TRYING TO DISCOVER A RADIO-ACTIVE ELEMENT. THEY MARRIED AND CONTINUED RESEARCH.

THE EMPEROR OF AUSTRIA GAVE THEM A TON OF PITCH-BLENDE FROM WHICH PIERRE AND MARIE HOPED TO EXTRACT ABOUT 1 GRAM OF RADIUM.

FOR MONTHS THEY WORKED, BOILING AND REFINING THE PITCH-BLENDE, UNTIL, AFTER FOUR YEARS HARD WORK —

THERE APPEARED A TINY GLOWING OBJECT IN A CRUCIBLE. 1/10 OF A GRAM OF RADIUM- THE FIRST THAT ANYONE HAD EVER SEEN.

TRAGEDY OVERTOOK THE CURIE'S. POOR PIERRE WAS KILLED IN A STREET ACCIDENT, AND MARIE WITH TWO YOUNG DAUGHTERS HAD TO CARRY ON ALONE.

HONOURS WERE SHOWERED UPON MME. CURIE, AND THE FAME OF HER DISCOVERY ECHOED ROUND THE WORLD.

IN THE 1914-18 WAR MME. CURIE WAS PLACED "IN CHARGE OF A RADIUM-THERAPY SECTION OF THE RED CROSS, AND HELPED TO SAVE MANY LIVES.

VAST SUMS OF MONEY WERE OFFERED TO HER FOR HER SECRET, BUT SHE REFUSED TO BENEFIT PERSONALLY. "OUR DISCOVERY IS FOR MANKIND ONLY" SHE SAID.

AS A RESULT, RADIUM HAS BECOME AVAILABLE TO COUNTRIES AND PEOPLES ALL OVER THE WORLD, AND HAS SAVED THE LIFE OF MILLIONS SUFFERING FROM DISEASE, PARTICULARLY CANCER VICTIMS.

Cinderella of Music

THE STORY OF

Eileen Joyce

BY JOHN BYRNE. ILLUSTRATED BY JOHN CHAMBERLAIN

INSIDE the rather shabby little town hall of Boulder City, Western Australia, there wasn't a spare inch of space. Every seat, every bit of standing room, was taken. Outside the hall, those who weren't lucky enough to get in, just stood and waited. For in that hot, dusty gold-mining town, four hundred miles from the sea, it was an occasion. More than twenty years before, Boulder City had sent one of its daughters out to conquer the world. She had conquered the world, her world, the world of music. And now in the late summer of 1948, she had come back home to show them.

Seated at the grand piano on the stage, and playing just as beautifully and as brilliantly as if she was in London's Albert Hall, was Eileen Joyce – one of Britain's most gifted and popular concert pianists.

With her dark red hair flowing around her shoulders, and her exotic dress of greeny-blue chiffon, she was the very picture of radiance. But a few people sitting in the hall that night saw beyond the beautiful and successful woman on the stage, and remembered the little girl, with untidy, tousled hair and feet unaccustomed to shoes who had set out to be a great pianist.

They remembered how she had left Boulder City with nothing but a scholarship to a convent. They remembered how, with great determination and spirit, she had fought her way to fame.

Born of parents so poor, that her home was a tent, and her first cradle an old kerosene tin, the tiny spark of her talent was nurtured and grew in the wilds of the Australian bush. Who could have guessed, then, that one day it would burst forth like a magic flame to delight the world? Her story is like a fairy tale, and well might she be called the Cinderella of music.

Eileen was born in Tasmania at a place called Zeehan in 1914. What date? Not even Eileen knows that. Her birth was not registered, there were no calendars in the home, and to Eileen's mother, one day was very like another in the hardship of their life in the bush. The day was just forgotten. Later, when Eileen first went to school, she found out about birthdays. She also found out that there was a patron saint of music, called Saint Cecilia.

One day she asked her mother what was the 'feast day' of this saint.

"It's November 21," said Mrs Joyce.

"Then that will be my birthday," said Eileen. And so it has remained. But Mrs Joyce was wrong about the saint's anniversary by one day. Saint Cecilia's day is November 22.

When Eileen was little more than two years old, the family moved to the mainland of Australia, for Eileen's father, John Joyce, wanted to prospect for gold.

So Eileen spent the early years of her childhood in

primitive and lonely mining camps, living the life of a Nomad, moving with her family from place to place in the fruitless search for gold.

Once somebody gave her an old mouth-organ, and this was Eileen's first contact with musical sound. Her mother was astonished at the speed and ease with which she learned to play it, imitating the bird sounds of the Australian bush, and picking up simple songs.

WHEN Eileen was nine, her father gave up the unequal struggle of trying to wrest gold from the stubborn ground, and decided to move to Boulder City, where his brother lived. He decided to take any sort of work, whether it be mining underground in the deep mines of what is called the 'Golden Mile', or else as a labourer.

For Eileen it was the beginning of life, for it was then she saw her first piano.

Her uncle kept an hotel in the hot, dirty little town, and in one of the back bars was an old piano with keys stained and yellowed with age, and notes sadly out of tune.

Eileen first saw the piano when her mother took her to visit her uncle. She was fascinated by it. She walked over and gingerly pressed some of the notes.

"Mummy," she asked Mrs Joyce, "can you play it?"

Laughingly her mother told her that she was no great pianist, but could play one or two tunes.

"Oh, please do," begged Eileen.

Mrs Joyce sat down and played 'The Campbells are Coming'. This was the first tune that Eileen learned to play. Later, her mother taught her 'Irish Diamonds'.

Now that the family was in Boulder, they were, by contrast, decently housed. They no longer lived in a tent, but, like hundreds of other mining families, had a shack made of wood and corrugated iron.

So in 1948 Eileen Joyce came back to Boulder City especially to give a concert in memory of her father. It was this concert with which I began this story. As a newspaper reporter, I was not only present at the concert, but accompanied her on a car trip around the town. I found out that her old home was still standing, and determined to take her there.

Eileen's mother was with her, and as they went around the little shack, which Eileen had not seen since she was a schoolgirl, she chatted away about where the furniture had once stood, and what colours the curtains had been. Earlier that day, when Eileen had arrived at the airport, a woman rushed out of the crowd, and breaking through the ring of relatives, thrust a bouquet of flowers into her arms.

"Why, Olive," said Eileen at once, "how good to see you again."

'Olive', now a music teacher herself, had learned the piano side by side with Eileen at their first lessons. Eileen had not seen her for more than twenty years, yet she remembered this fellow pupil perfectly, and immediately began to recall memories of their early lessons together.

Eileen Joyce has indeed an extraordinary memory, a strong asset, if not a necessity for a great pianist.

But to return to her story.

"Mummy," she asked Mrs Joyce, "can you play the piano?"

Eileen was sent to the convent school in Boulder City. She didn't care for ordinary lessons much, but soon discovered that it was possible to learn to play the piano. She was overjoyed. Here was something she really wanted to do. But it wasn't as easy as all that, for music lessons cost sixpence, and to the Joyce family, sixpence was a lot of money. But Eileen plagued her family until the money was found.

In half the time it took the other children to be ready for their preliminary examinations in music, Eileen was ready for her Intermediate -- an exam which was difficult for students several years older than she was. Eileen not only passed, but passed with honours.

It was time, thought the nuns at Boulder City, that something was done about Eileen Joyce.

The Parish Priest was called in. He listened to Eileen play. That night he wrote to the Reverend Mother of the Loreto Convent in Perth, the capital city, and it was arranged that Eileen should go to this convent to be taught music by a Sister John, a teacher of great ability.

Somehow or other the Joyce family raked up the money to pay for Eileen's fare to Perth and for her school uniform. Perhaps Eileen's fairy godmother had waved her magic wand.

EILEEN was happy at Loreto Convent. She worked hard and made astounding progress. She found in Sister John a teacher not only of competence but of sympathy and understanding. But what was to happen to her when her time at the convent was over?

Then fate, as it often does, took a hand. Or perhaps it was the fairy godmother again.

Two world famous pianists heard Eileen play. Visiting musical celebrities often came to the convent when they were in Perth to play for the nuns, and two of these were the composer-pianist Percy Granger, and the German concert pianist Wilhelm Backhaus. Both men were in complete agreement. This child had great talent and must study at Leipzig – the great German centre of music. But how could the teen-age daughter of a poor miner possibly hope to get to Leipzig?

But word had got about that here was a child who was a musical genius. Under the guidance of a Perth business-man, a fund called the 'Eileen Joyce Fund' was set up, and concerts were organised all over Western Australia to raise money. At some of these, Eileen played herself – a small, shy figure in a white dress.

Soon £900 had been raised. Enough to send her half-way round the world to Leipzig.

This was Eileen's big chance, and she lived up to her opportunity. For two years she worked every available moment, practising, going to lessons, and practising again.

Just when she felt that she was really making progress, and that one day she really would be a first class pianist, disaster overtook her.

She had completed two years at the Leipzig Conservatorium when she developed a bad foot. For over a month she was in hospital, haunted by the fear not only that it was costing too much money, but that perhaps her foot would never be strong enough or flexible enough to work the piano pedals. After a few weeks' rest her foot was cured, but not her money troubles.

The authorities who controlled her finances sent for her and said that very little of her original £900 was left. She had enough for one more term. Then she must get more money from Australia or else go back home.

That night Eileen went to hear Tchaikovsky's Concerto No 1 of which she is very fond. When she got to the hall, she was late, and the door was shut. There was nothing to do but sit on the steps and wait until the first movement was over.

Eileen, overcome not only with this little disappointment, but with all her other troubles as well, sat down and cried, like Cinderella among the ashes.

Then appeared Cinderella's fairy godmother, or to be more accurate, two fairy godmothers, in the forms of Mr and Mrs Andreae, a wealthy couple from New Zealand, then living in England, whose love of music had brought them to Leipzig. They, too, were late for the concert and saw the forlorn figure sitting on the steps.

"We people from the Dominions must stick together," said Mr Andreae when he'd heard Eileen's story. He and his wife undertook to pay for the rest of Eileen's studies at Leipzig and see what they could do about getting her the right start on the English concert platform.

AND SO it was arranged. Eileen made her professional debut in the now bombed Queen's Hall in London on September 30, 1930, as soloist at a coveted promenade concert.

Cinderella had arrived at her ball. In a flowing concert gown which the Andreaes provided for her, she was hardly recognisable as the little girl who had left Australia three years before, and, like Cinderella, she was a sensation.

But there was still a struggle ahead. She was just a young girl who had played very well at one concert. What could she do to get people to take more notice of her?

Eileen's solution was to try and make records of her playing, but at first she could not get a single recording company interested. She stormed their offices and made frantic appeals that all she needed was a chance to show them. Finally, one company relented, and Eileen was allowed to make a record. It was not only a success – it was a best seller!

From then on Eileen appeared regularly at Prom concerts and got occasional engagements in the provinces. She also did quite a lot of broadcasting. Due to her hard work at this time and her fabulous memory, she can now play almost *sixty* piano concertos and other works with orchestra.

It was the fine quality of her records which first brought her attention, and she gained a large unseen audience. But it was not until the war that the general public got to know her better and raised her to the place of popularity where she is today.

She toured all over the country with the London Philharmonic Orchestra, bringing the solace of fine music to the people in blitzed towns. She shared the honours of soloist with the famous pianist Moiseiwitch.

After the war, Eileen Joyce began to work in films. She appeared first in a film called *A Girl in a Million* and then in *Battle for Music* – a title which could not have been more appropriate in her case. If you ever saw that

and elegance of dress. She has hair of a deep copper colour, and, offstage, the vivacity and wit that usually goes with this colouring.

Because she is a pianist, her hands have always received a great deal of care, and although they are smooth and white, they contrast strangely with the rest of her appearance. Instead of long, slim fingers, she has strong, blunt hands, in shape like a working man's. The sinews and muscles are well-developed and powerful from the six hours of

They, too, were late for the concert and saw a forlorn figure sitting on the steps.

fine film *The Seventh Veil*, starring Ann Todd as a concert pianist, those were Eileen's hands at the keyboard, not Miss Todd's. She also played the sound track of *Brief Encounter* and *Quartet*, and more recently, she appeared briefly in *Trent's Last Case*.

Eileen Joyce has also had a film made about her life as a child. It is called *Wherever She Goes*, and is taken from a book about her called *Prelude*. Eileen also played the sound track music for this film.

If you have ever seen her in a film, or been to one of her concerts, you will know that not only is she a great pianist, but also a woman of great charm of appearance

practice (sometimes more) which she does every day.

If ever you go to hear her play, you may notice that at the beginning of the concert, she is wearing, for example, a white dress with her hair down. But when she comes on the stage to play again, she has changed completely, and is now in green with her hair upswept. It is as if, like Cinderella again, her fairy godmother was standing in the wings and with a wave of her wand, had given her a complete change of clothes.

Some music critics once told Eileen that they did not approve of the several changes which she makes during a concert. Eileen replied: "Would the critics prefer I wear black? Changing fills in the intervals when I might be biting my nails with nervousness." She also said that she grows hot and exhausted while playing, and a change of clothes and hair style refresh her.

I once heard someone say that Eileen Joyce fitted her clothes to the music she was playing. "She wears sequins for Debussy, green when she's playing Chopin, red and gold when the composer is Schumann, and her hair up for Beethoven and down for Grieg," he said.

Though something as detailed as this is slightly absurd, and is not true, Eileen does agree that some colours and composers do go together.

"If I am playing the classics, I wear something classical both in colour and design. If I am playing Tchaikovsky, I like to wear brilliant colours," she says.

After her ragged childhood, and the years of her girlhood when she was studying hard and had no time for the parties and dances which other girls of her age went to, it would not be at all surprising if, deep down, there is still a child's love of 'dressing up' in Eileen Joyce.

Most famous people have some mascot or other without which they would not make a public appearance, and Eileen's is a small cross which always accompanies her to the concert platform. She also has a small and beautiful leopard skin muff which she wears to the piano, and which rests by the side of the keys while she is playing. Few people know that inside it is a tiny hot water bottle for warmth. With a pianist it is most important that the hands do not get cold, for numb, unfeeling fingers cannot cope with intricate patterns of notes.

Before every concert she rehearses for several hours, then rests for an hour before dressing and drinking an egg whipped in milk – her only meal before playing in public. On an ordinary day she gets up at 8 a.m., practises from 9 a.m. until lunch time, goes horse-riding, or sleeps until tea, then does a further two hours' practice. She is usually in bed by 9 p.m.

Her home is a fourteen-room house, with 150 acres of farmland, in the beautiful Thames Valley. Upstairs, in one of the large rooms, are her practice pianos, two beautiful and perfectly tuned instruments, which she plays on alternately as the whim takes her.

It is, indeed, a far cry from these two wonderful pianos and the beautiful and talented woman who plays them, to the little girl with no shoes who learned to play on the broken and yellowed notes of an old relic of a piano, and whose first music lesson cost sixpence.

Just like a fairy story. Just like Cinderella.

Do you want to be a KENNEL MAID?

ANNE LOVES DOGS AND IS GOING TO TRAIN AS A KENNEL MAID WHEN SHE LEAVES SCHOOL.

COME TO HEEL, ROUGH!

ANNE, WHO BEGINS AT THE KENNELS IN A WEEK'S TIME, IS TAKING HER DOG ROUGH OUT FOR HIS USUAL WALK. HER TRAINING OF HIM WILL PROVE VERY USEFUL IN HER NEW JOB.

THE KENNELS ARE NEAR ANNE'S HOME, WHICH MEANS SHE CAN COME IN EACH DAY INSTEAD OF BEING A RESIDENT STUDENT. SHE PAYS TWO GUINEAS A WEEK FOR HER TRAINING.

THIS IS BRUNO, THE PET OF THE KENNELS.

HE'S SWEET. I LIKE SPANIELS BEST OF ALL, I THINK.

WILL YOU EXPLAIN THAT BIT AGAIN, PLEASE?

YES, OF COURSE. NOW LISTEN CAREFULLY...

DURING HER FIRST YEAR, ANNE ATTENDS A WEEKLY LECTURE BY THE LOCAL VETERINARY SURGEON ON THE CARE AND ANATOMY OF ALL BREEDS OF DOGS.

WHAT A CROWD! I'M GLAD YOU WERE ABLE TO GET SEATS, DADDY.

YES, I WAS VERY LUCKY.

ANNE IS CELEBRATING A SUCCESSFULLY COMPLETED FIRST YEAR AS A KENNEL MAID. SHE WILL GET A REDUCTION OF HER FEES FOR THE SECOND AND FINAL YEAR.

PART OF ANNE'S JOB IS PREPARING DOGS FOR THE SHOW RING. SHE IS SHOWN HOW TO TRIM THEM AND HOW TO PRESENT THEM TO THE JUDGES.

HE LOOKS A PICTURE, DOESN'T HE?

SEE THAT HE KEEPS HIS HEAD UP, ANNE.

HE OUGHT TO— I'VE SPENT NEARLY ALL THE MORNING GROOMING HIM!

I MUST RING HOME AND TELL THEM I'LL BE LATE, JUNE.

RIGHT—HO, ANNE, I'LL WAIT OUTSIDE FOR YOU.

NOW ALMOST AT THE END OF HER SECOND YEAR, ANNE OFTEN HAS TO CANCEL APPOINTMENTS WHEN A LITTER OF PUPPIES IS EXPECTED, AND HER HOURS OF WORK ARE NEVER VERY CERTAIN.

ONE OF THE JOBS ANNE LIKES BEST IS EXERCISING THE DOGS. SHE HAS NOW FINISHED HER TWO YEARS' TRAINING, BUT IS STAYING ON AT THE KENNELS AND HAS MORE RESPONSIBLE WORK TO DO.

HELLO, ANNE WHEN ARE YOU GOING TO FORSAKE DOGS FOR HORSES?

I'LL NEVER DO THAT NEIL. I LOVE THE KENNELS.

ANNE IS VISITING HER FRIEND JUNE WHO TRAINED WITH HER AT THE KENNELS. JUNE IS NOW A SALESWOMAN IN A DOG SHOP.

IT'S A LOVELY SHOP, JUNE.

I LIKE WORKING HERE BETTER THAN AT THE KENNELS.

HAVE A TALK TO YOUR PARENTS, ANNE, AND LET ME KNOW WHAT THEY THINK.

ALL RIGHT. I'LL GIVE YOU A DEFINITE ANSWER TOMORROW.

AFTER FIVE YEARS AT THE KENNELS, ANNE WANTS A CHANGE. THE LOCAL VET HAS ASKED HER TO BE HIS KENNEL MAID. THIS MEANS HELPING WITH OPERATIONS AND TREATING SICK DOGS.

BRING HER IN, JIMMY, AND LET ME HAVE A LOOK AT HER.

SHE'S MUCH BETTER THIS WEEK, MISS.

ANNE HAS NOW BEGUN HER NEW JOB. SHE OFTEN HAS TO GO OUT AT NIGHT WITH THE VET WHEN ANIMALS ARE ILL, AND HER LIFE IS A BUSY AND EXCITING ONE. WE HOPE YOU WILL BE AS HAPPY AS SHE IS

SOME BRITISH BIRDS…

CRESTED TIT

WRYNECK

TREE CREEPER

BY PETER KNEEBONE

CAPERCAILLIE

HOBBY

RING OUZEL

SANDWICH TERN

AVOCET

MARTINE and the MYSTERY OF THE GOLDEN BUDDHA

Story by **BETTY ROLAND**

Drawn by **CHARLES PAINE**

MARTINE IS A FRENCH GIRL LIVING WITH HER FATHER, COLONEL LEFEVRE, IN INDO-CHINA. ONE DAY AS SHE AND HER FRIEND LOTUS FLOWER ARE CROSSING THE BARRACK SQUARE . . . .

WHY, PAPA, WHAT IS THE MATTER?

BAD NEWS, MARTINE. HUAN MING AND HIS BANDITS HAVE RAIDED ANOTHER TOWN. THEY MUST BE CAUGHT OR IT MEANS DISGRACE FOR ME AND MY REGIMENT.

DISGRACE FOR THE REGIMENT! WHY, PAPA?

I HAVE ORDERS TO CAPTURE HUAN MING IMMEDIATELY AND IT IS LIKE TRYING TO CATCH CHAIN LIGHTNING. HE IS NEVER IN THE SAME PLACE TWICE.

HERE ARE YOUR HORSES. HAVE A GOOD RIDE, BUT DON'T BE LATE GETTING HOME.

WHAT WILL YOU GIVE US IF WE FIND HUAN MING, PAPA?

A PARADE WITH FULL MILITARY HONOURS!

LATER . . .

MARTINE, LOOK— A STORM IS BLOWING UP.

AND IT'S FIVE O'CLOCK. WE MUST TURN BACK, LOTUS FLOWER.

HERE COMES THE RAIN! WE'D BETTER TAKE SHELTER IN THAT RUINED TEMPLE UP THERE.

JUST MADE IT! WHAT A QUEER OLD PLACE THIS IS. LET'S GO INSIDE AND LOOK AROUND.

NO, NO! BETTER THAT WE STAY OUT HERE. TOO DARK INSIDE.

DON'T WORRY, LOTUS FLOWER, THESE TWIGS WILL GIVE US LIGHT TO SEE BY.

JUST LOOK AT THAT GREAT GOLDEN BUDDHA UP THERE!

IT IS VERY STRANGE FOR A BUDDHA LIKE THAT TO BE IN A RUINED TEMPLE. HE HAS MUCH GOLD AND JEWELS. BUT WAIT...

...PUT OUT THAT LIGHT. I HEAR VOICES. PEOPLE ARE COMING UP THE PATH TOWARDS THE TEMPLE.

MARTINE, HIDE! HIDE FOR OUR LIVES!

WHY, WHAT'S THE MATTER, LOTUS FLOWER? WHY ARE YOU AFRAID?

LOOK AT THE CAP OF THE LEADER. IT IS THE DREADED WHITE PLUME OF THE BANDIT, HUAN MING!

WHERE CAN WE HIDE SO THAT THEY WILL NOT SEE US?

UP THERE, ON THOSE BEAMS OF WOOD.

WE'RE JUST IN TIME. HERE THEY COME.

SSH — LISTEN TO WHAT THEY SAY.

YOU HAVE DONE WELL, MY MEN. WE HAVE MUCH LOOT FROM THE RECENT RAIDS. YOUR LEADER, HUAN MING, IS PLEASED WITH YOU...

...AND THE LOVING FRIENDS OF OUR PRISONER HERE, THE RICH MERCHANT FROM SIAM, WILL PAY MUCH GOLD TO SEE HIM AGAIN!

AT DAWN TOMORROW, AS COLONEL LEFEVRE AND HIS MEN RIDE THROUGH THE DEVIL'S PASS, WE WILL SWOOP DOWN AND DESTROY THEM. THEN MING AND HIS YELLOW HAWKS WILL RULE THE COUNTRY UNOPPOSED.

HURRAH FOR MING!

THEY MEAN TO AMBUSH MY FATHER AND HIS MEN!

NOW THE GOLDEN BUDDHA REVEALS HIS SECRET. BE READY TO TAKE THE TREASURE TO OUR HIDING PLACE BELOW.

LOOK, LOTUS FLOWER — LOOK! THE STEPS HAVE ROLLED AWAY. THERE MUST BE A CAVE UNDER THE TEMPLE.

I SEE IT ALL, MARTINE.

YOU TWO KEEP WATCH UP HERE WHILE I AM BELOW.

OUR EYES SHALL NEVER CLOSE, O MING.

LOTUS FLOWER, WE MUST WARN MY FATHER!

BUT WE DARE NOT MOVE WHILE THOSE TWO MEN REMAIN DOWN THERE.

WHERE HAVE YOU COME FROM AND WHAT IS YOUR NAME?

YOU REFUSE TO TELL ME? VERY WELL, MING KNOWS HOW TO LOOSEN OBSTINATE TONGUES!

TAKE THE PRISONER DOWN BELOW!

NO MATTER WHAT HAPPENS, I MUST NOT TELL MING WHO I AM.

THIS IS THE SECRET OF THE GOLDEN BUDDHA. LOOK YOUR FILL, FOR YOU WILL NEVER LIVE TO TELL WHAT YOU SEE.

WHY, IT'S LIKE ALADDIN'S CAVE!

FOR THE LAST TIME, WILL YOU TELL ME WHO YOU ARE?

FOR THE LAST TIME, NO!

TAKE HER AWAY, MEN. YOU KNOW HOW TO MAKE HER TALK.

WAIT! STOP!

WHAT DO YOU WANT?

I KNOW WHO SHE IS!

LOUIE TONG, MY FATHER'S GROOM!

SHE IS THE DAUGHTER OF OUR ENEMY, COLONEL LEFEVRE!

THE DAUGHTER OF COLONEL LEFEVRE! IS IT POSSIBLE?

THIS IS MAGNIFICENT NEWS! YOU SHALL BE RICHLY REWARDED FOR THIS.

WHAT IS THE REWARD FOR TREACHERY, LOUIE TONG?

YOUR HONOURABLE FATHER WILL SOON WISH YOU HAD NEVER LEFT FRANCE.

MY HONOURABLE FATHER WILL SOON MAKE YOU WISH YOU HAD NEVER BEEN BORN!

FASTEN HER SECURELY WITH THIS ROPE. THEN WE WILL ALL SIT IN COUNCIL AND MAKE PLANS.

LOTUS FLOWER, I HOPE YOU'RE ON YOUR WAY BACK TO THE BARRACKS. I NEED HELP BADLY!

BUT LOTUS FLOWER IS HAVING TROUBLES OF HER OWN....

THE HORSES HAVE TAKEN FRIGHT AND BROKEN AWAY. WHAT SHALL I DO?

I'LL NEVER GET TO THE BARRACKS IN TIME, BUT THIS GOAT TRACK MAY BE A SHORT CUT THROUGH THE HILLS.

THERE'S A LIGHT DOWN THERE IN THE VALLEY. DARE I ASK FOR HELP? WHOEVER IT IS MAY BE IN LEAGUE WITH HUAN MING.

WHY, IT'S AN OLD GOATHERD! I'LL TAKE A CHANCE AND ASK HIM FOR AID.

WHO ARE YOU, AND WHAT DO YOU WANT?

I AM LOST. CAN YOU SHOW ME A PATH THROUGH THE HILLS?

MEANWHILE THE ALARM HAS ALREADY SPREAD TO THE BARRACKS.

COLONEL, COME QUICKLY! THE HORSES HAVE RETURNED WITHOUT THEIR RIDERS!

WHAT!

MARTINE MUST HAVE HAD AN ACCIDENT. SOUND THE ALARM AND ORGANIZE A SEARCH PARTY AT ONCE!

YES, COLONEL.

THEY WERE LAST SEEN RIDING INTO THE HILLS. YOU TAKE THE WESTERN ROUTE, LIEUTENANT, AND I'LL TAKE THE OTHER.

DO NOT DESPAIR, SIR. PERHAPS THEY TOOK SHELTER FROM THE STORM.

WHAT A NIGHT IN WHICH TO SEARCH FOR TWO GIRLS LOST IN THESE DESOLATE HILLS! MARTINE, MY LITTLE ONE, WHERE ARE YOU?

IF COLONEL LEFEVRE HAD ONLY KNOWN . . . . .

WE HAVE MADE OUR PLANS. YOU ARE COMING WITH US.

WHERE ARE YOU TAKING ME?

TO DEVIL'S PASS—TO SEE THE SURPRISE WE HAVE PREPARED FOR YOUR FATHER AND HIS GALLANT MEN.

TAKE CARE, MING! THERE MAY BE AN EVEN BIGGER SURPRISE FOR YOU!

THE PRISONER IS INSOLENT! BIND HER MOUTH SO THAT SHE IS SILENT.

SO THAT I CAN'T WARN MY FATHER, YOU MEAN!

ONCE MORE THE GOLDEN BUDDHA GUARDS OUR SECRET. SOON WE HIDE NO LONGER HUAN MING BE GREAT WAR-LORD AND YOU MEN HIS TRUSTED GENERALS.

HAIL, MIGHTY MING!

HURRAH FOR MING!

IT IS STILL TWO HOURS TILL DAWN. WE HAVE GOOD TIME TO PREPARE OUR ATTACK.

WE WAIT FOR YOUR ORDERS, MING.

HERE IS DEVIL'S PASS. TAKE COVER. TRAIN YOUR GUNS ON ROAD AND FIRE WHEN I GIVE WORD.

ALL SHALL BE AS YOU SAY, MING.

LOTUS FLOWER, DID YOU GET THERE IN TIME?

LOOK, THE SOLDIERS COME!

CARRY OUT YOUR ORDERS THEN, YOU KNOW WHAT TO DO.

WHAT DOES THIS MEAN? I DO NOT LIKE IT.

RIDE AHEAD OF US, GIRL. IF YOU TRY TO RUN AWAY I WILL SHOOT!

WE WANT YOU TO SEE THE WELCOME THAT WE GIVE YOUR FATHER.

YES. HERE YOU GET GOOD VIEW OF EVERYTHING.

THEY ARE NOT MORE THAN TWENTY YARDS AWAY.

GOOD! NOW WE GIVE THEM BIG SURPRISE.

COLONEL LEFEVRE, YOU ARE SURROUNDED ON EVERY SIDE. HALT, OR I GIVE ORDERS TO FIRE!

TEN PACES FURTHER AND YOU ARE ALL DEAD MEN!

THEY DO NOT SEEM TO HEAR YOU. PERHAPS THEY SLEEP.

I WILL SOON WAKE THEM! *OPEN FIRE!*

WHAT.....?

THEY ARE NOT MEN, BUT DUMMIES. WE'VE BEEN TRICKED!

AND LOOK, HERE COME THE REAL MEN.

THOUSAND CURSES ON THE CUNNING WHITE MAN!

RIDE FOR YOUR LIFE! THIS WAY!

LOTUS FLOWER, YOU GOT THERE IN TIME. HURRAH!

BUT THERE WAS NO ESCAPE FOR HUAN MING....

MORE SOLDIERS. WE ARE TRAPPED.

AYE-E-E-E!

THERE GOES HUAN MING. AFTER HIM, MEN!

Margot Fonteyn, the first Sadler's Wells ballerina of international fame.

Moira Shearer as the Princess Aurora in *The Sleeping Beauty*.

Violetta Elvin, one of the few Sadler's Wells dancers to achieve fame before joining the Company.

Beryl Grey as Giselle, in Act II of the ballet of the same name.

BELLE *of the* BALLET

Written by:
GEORGE BEARDMORE
Drawn by:
CHRIS GARVEY

CRAZY DAY

BELLE AND HER FRIENDS ARE PUPILS AT THE ARENSKA SCHOOL OF DANCING IN LONDON. THEY HAVE PROMISED TO GIVE A DISPLAY OF DANCING AT A GIRLS' ORPHANAGE IN THE COUNTRY, BUT IT'S PERFECTLY CLEAR FROM THE START THAT THIS IS ONE OF THOSE DAYS WHEN EVERYTHING GOES WRONG...

WE MUST RUSH GIRLS. WHERE'S BELLE?

MM-MM-MM-MM!

BELLE, HOW CHANGED YOU ARE!

DON'T BE SILLY, DAVID. *PLEASE* HELP ME GET THIS MASK OFF!

COME, AS YOU ARE! WE'RE 40 MINUTES LATE.

I SHALL HAVE TO STEP ON IT. PACEBURY ORPHANAGE IS SEVENTY-EIGHT MILES AWAY.

HOORAY, MY HEAD'S COMING OFF!

NOW WE CAN SETTLE DOWN TO A GOOD LONG RUN.

DON'T YOU BELIEVE IT, HONEY. IT'S ONE OF THOSE CRAZY DAYS.

AND HALF-AN-HOUR LATER...

WATCH OUT, DAVID!

ANY BONES BROKEN?

NO. BUT HOW DO WE GET TO PACEBURY, NOW?

TRAMP IT, HONEY. ONLY ANOTHER 40 MILES!

THIS GARAGE WILL LOOK AFTER THE CAR.

DO YOU THINK WE CAN MAKE THAT TRAIN?

LET'S TRY!

HERE'S AN EMPTY ONE!

BUT IT'S RESERVED!

AS THEY SPEED ALONG KATIE IS SO LOST IN WONDER THAT—

— OH, DEAR!

AND AT THE ORPHANAGE...

SO YOU LOST THE CASE, DID YOU, KATIE?

YES, MISS RILEY.

THEN I FORBID YOU TO ATTEND THE PERFORMANCE.

DO LET HER COME, MISS RILEY, PLEASE! IT WAS OUR FAULT.

I HAVE GIVEN MY ORDERS. KINDLY PROCEED WITH THE PERFORMANCE.

WITHOUT COSTUMES IT'LL BE THE BIGGEST, FLOP EVER, BELLE!

MAMIE IS RIGHT, AND A CURTAIN MUST BE DRAWN OVER THE MOST MISERABLE PERFORMANCE IN BELLE'S CAREER. WITHOUT COSTUMES THE ANIMAL BALLET BECOMES MEANINGLESS AND SILLY.

KATIE PROVIDES THE ONLY BRIGHT SPOT OF THE EVENING...

FORBIDDEN TO GO IN AT THE FRONT, SHE TRIES THE BACK, WITH DIRE CONSEQUENCES...

... BUT FINDS ANOTHER CHAMPION IN MRS MORRIS ...

PLEASE DON'T BE CROSS WITH HER, MISS RILEY. LET HER SIT WITH ME.

WHEN THE CURTAIN FALLS, KATIE ALONE CLAPS...

AND KATIE ALONE SEES THEM OFF...

BYE-BYE, KATIE. YOU'RE SURE OF THAT TRAIN, ARE YOU?

YES, THE 6.40. IT'S THE LAST TRAIN. GOODBYE!

BUT AT THE STATION...

SORRY, MISS, THE 6.40 DOESN'T RUN ON SATURDAY. THE LAST TRAIN'S GONE.

KATIE AGAIN! THIS MEANS SLEEPING AT THE ORPHANAGE.

I WONDER IF SHE DID IT ON PURPOSE?

RICHARD

Meet one of Britain's brightest stars

BURTON

by Maud Miller

Illustrated by Eric Dadswell

W HENEVER I think of Richard Burton, two other famous names come to mind . . . Emlyn Williams, and Dylan Thomas.

Three famous people linked together by circumstance and who have one thing in common, the land of their birth, Wales.

Richard Burton got his first chance as a professional actor from Emlyn Williams, the famous actor and playwright, and made his name in radio in the first performance of *Under Milk Wood*, by Dylan Thomas.

But let us begin at the beginning.

Richard was born in a mining village, Pontrydyfen, in South Wales. His real name is Richard Jenkins. He took the name of Burton from the man who adopted him when he was twelve and who helped to give him a love of acting, Mr P. H. Burton – a producer in the Welsh Home Service of the B.B.C. and also a great friend of Dylan Thomas.

When he was two, Richard's mother died, and an older sister took on the job of bringing him up.

He was very much like any of the other boys in the village. He went to school in Port Talbot, was very keen on rugby football, and learnt to ride bareback on pit ponies in holiday times.

That early training came in handy when he made *Alexander the Great* and discovered that he was expected to tear round the battlefields on a horse without the benefit of a saddle!

The lad who was to grow up to be one of the best Shakespearean actors of his time learnt his Shakespeare in the nicest possible way.

He had a schoolmaster who took the drudgery out of the process by making the class act the plays instead of learning them by heart. Richard often used to sit up half the night reciting Shakespeare to himself, playing all the parts.

He was keen to learn and went to a secondary school, took his Matric, and then won a scholarship to Oxford. Before he was old enough to go there, however, he saw an advertisement for someone to play a Welsh part in a play.

The play was *The Druid's Rest*, the author was Emlyn Williams, who was also the star and the producer of the play.

"I intended the part for someone much older than Richard," Emlyn Williams once told me. "I had thought of someone about 22, but Richard was so excellent when he read the part for me, that I gave him the benefit of the doubt about his age!"

"Like most beginners," Emlyn relates, "he would not, or could not, learn to close a stage door without slamming it. I had to remind him, before every performance: 'DON'T SLAM THE DOOR, RICHARD'. Soon it became quite a joke."

Ever since then, when Richard has a first night of any new performance, he receives a good-luck telegram from Emlyn Williams, as a reminder. In the case of his celebrated *Hamlet*, at the Old Vic, the telegram said: "Don't slam the castle gates, Richard!"

Seventeen-year-old Burton was a fair success in that modest rôle in *The Druid's Rest*, and made his first acquaintance with London Town at the same time.

Also in the cast was another young actor, Stanley Baker. The two boys discovered they were from the same part of 'The Valley'. They had never met before, but at Stanley's school, one of his chums was a girl called Sybil Williams, who had known Richard most of her young life. She grew up and became Mrs Richard Burton.

When the time came for him to take up his Oxford Scholarship, Richard had to leave the cast of *The Druid's Rest*, but he managed to find time for acting with the University dramatic society, in the intervals of studying his chosen subjects, English, Italian and Literature.

His studies were cut short by the war, when he joined the R.A.F. and was sent to Canada to train as a navigator.

When the war ended Richard began his acting career all over again, and it wasn't long before he was appearing in first-class rôles in London, New York and Stratford-on-Avon.

His first film, *The Last Days of Dolwyn*, came through Emlyn Williams . . . yes, Emlyn Williams again!

The latter wrote the story of the film for that great Welsh actress, Dame Edith Evans. He directed the film and played one of the principal parts as well.

It was the story of a Welsh village, and why it was flooded and turned into a great lake. Richard was *really* 22 then, and played the part of the young romantic hero.

Says Richard, of this adventure, "I was scared I would over-act. When I saw myself on the screen I crawled out of the cinema!"

It is characteristic of Burton that he is shy of his own image, and rarely sits through the whole of any of his films.

In the theatre, too, he prefers not to have his wife at first nights. He'd rather she waited till about the sixth night, "when I've rubbed off the rough edges," as he puts it.

His Hamlet was one of the highlights of the 1951

A scene from 'The Last Days of Dolwyn', Richard's first film, in which he played opposite that great actress, Edith Evans.

Richard's Hamlet
was one of the highlights
of the 1951 *season at Stratford.*

season at Stratford . . . and then things really began to happen!

A contract with Sir Alexander Korda . . . and all Hollywood hot on his trail.

As Korda had no film ready for him at that time, he obligingly 'lent' Richard to 20th Century Fox, in Hollywood, for his first big rôle, opposite Olivia de Havilland, in *My Cousin Rachel*.

Burton made more impression on Hollywood than did Hollywood on Richard Burton, who had not much time for anything but work, and meeting a few old friends like James Mason, Jean Simons and Stewart Granger.

And then, even before he had completed *My Cousin Rachel,* the 20th Century boss, Darryl Zanuck, was cabling Korda to make arrangements to borrow Burton once again, for *Desert Rats*.

This was a modern story, about the defence of Tobruk, and made a good contrast to the costume rôle Richard had played in *My Cousin Rachel*.

There was also a lot of excitement in Hollywood about this time, over the new wide-screen processes. CinemaScope was being tried and tested, and Zanuck wanted Richard Burton for the lead in the first film . . . *The Robe,* a million-dollar production.

So, in 1953, Richard Burton became the first star of CinemaScope, as Marcellus the slave who defied the Emperor Caligula.

After that Darryl Zanuck wanted Richard to become a permanent fixture in Hollywood.

Richard said "No", quite politely, but quite firmly. His mind was made up for a return to the stage, so he came home again to play Hamlet at the Edinburgh Festival, and spent the season at the Old Vic.

In the end he got his own way, about Hollywood, agreeing to make one film a year for 20th Century, leaving himself free for Alexander Korda, or any other film producer, and also for the stage.

It was the same year, too, that Dylan Thomas so

tragically died during a visit to New York. His last work, *Under Milk Wood*, was written for the radio, and had already been scheduled for broadcasting, by a Welsh cast, with Dylan himself as the Narrator.

Rather than postpone the broadcast, Richard undertook to learn the part of the Narrator at short notice. Between his rehearsals at the Old Vic he learnt the long and difficult rôle.

Richard has done other things in radio – good things, too, but this remains his finest, for there was love in it, as well as technical skill.

In his next film in Hollywood, *The Prince of Players*, Burton had the odd experience of acting Shakespeare, in his rôle as another actor! That was because he played Edwin Booth, an American actor, who lived in the last century. Richard had to forget his own ideas of Shakespeare, and learn Booth's technique by reading old documents and newspaper cuttings.

The Prince of Players was very different from his next film, *Alexander the Great*.

For this he spent nearly six months in Spain, fighting Alexander's battles, in blazing sunshine, riding bareback. There were 150 speaking parts, in addition to the eight stars, and supporting rôles.

For the first time since they appeared together in *The Druid's Rest*, Richard found his friend Stanley Baker again, this time playing Attalus.

As it was such a long trip, Richard took some of his family along . . . his wife, a sister and brother-in-law, Ivor, who got leave of absence from the firm of builders who employ him, and a niece.

They did not enjoy the bull-fights, but thought they had better show up, as is the custom in Spain. Richard, who used to play rugby for the London Welsh, and Aberavon, remarked to Stanley Baker that he would sooner be watching the boys play rugger at Cardiff.

Then there were occasions when the Welsh contingent varied the music of the Spanish guitars in the evenings, by breaking into the Welsh National Anthem and other choral works.

For all his fame as an international stage and screen star, Burton has retained his native 'Welshness'. He remains at heart the boy from the Valleys, with a great love for his own home and his own people.

To them he is still 'Ritchie Jenkins'. There are many who think it is a pity he went in for 'the acting' and would have liked him to make rugby football his career.

"That Ritchie Jenkins," you'll hear them say, "he would have made the grade in first-class rugby!"

It is always back to the Valleys for Burton, when he comes home from Hollywood, or anywhere else. He is the only one of his family to go in for acting. His brothers are people with ordinary jobs . . . miner, bricklayer, council clerk, Army sergeant-major, colliery fitter.

His friends, and Sybil's friends, are 'ordinary' people, too, proud that Ritchie has done well for himself, but not envious of his success.

Nor does he stay at any expensive hotel when he's back home. It is the little house in Talbach, and the tiny bedroom he had as a boy in his sister's home, lit with one gas jet.

He likes it that way, likes to be called 'Ritchie' and slapped on the back by his miner friends on their way home from the pits.

CINDERS

By MEVIN

ACTOR
in the house

KENNETH MORE SOLVES
HIS FAMILY'S PROBLEM:
"WHAT SHALL WE DO WITH KENNY?"

BY MAUD MILLER

ILLUSTRATED BY BILL DOWSETT

IF you met Kenneth More anywhere by accident you would recognize him immediately. He looks so much like the characters he plays on the stage and screen, for which he needs very little make-up. Film star, stage star, or plain Kenneth More, he gets as much fun just being himself in most of his rôles as we do just watching the fun!

In real life he has the same breezy, easy personality. He is friendly with everyone and has a sense of humour that is second to none.

If you never saw 'Genevieve', Kenneth More's first major film success, you need not despair. This rather elderly film has become a classic and is revived from time to time, when cinema-managers feel their box-office is in need of a tonic!

The man who made that film such a smash-hit is a naturally gay person. But he can be quiet and thoughtful; he can be a serious straight actor, too, as in his

screen rôle of the leg-less hero, Wing Commander Douglas Bader, in 'Reach for the Sky'.

More's favourite sport is golf, and like most golfers he regards the business of reducing his handicap as all important, and works at it as though it were a challenge.

Golf is as important in the story of Kenneth More as his fancy waistcoats – with one big difference! The fancy waistcoats were invented as a special gag for 'Genevieve' and the idea was used again for 'Doctor in the House'. He does NOT wear fancy waistcoats at home.

In private life he prefers a quiet, casual style of dressing and, for all his exuberance, likes a quiet home life.

He made his world début at Gerrards Cross in September, 1915. His father, a Civil Engineer, suddenly became rich overnight when a relative died, and he inherited £60,000.

Kenneth's father was not a thrifty man, not the kind who saved for a rainy day. According to Kenneth: "It was for my sister and me a childhood of luxury."

When he was six the family went to live in Jersey, in the Channel Islands. Here Kenneth was educated at the Victoria College, where he got his first taste of acting.

He did not like it at all.

Because he had fair, curly hair he was cast as Juliet

and Olivia in school performances of Shakespeare. He collected a lot of black eyes and bruises, fighting with other boys to prove he was not a sissy.

His first ambition was to become a surgeon – till he discovered that a lot of swotting was involved, including mathematics, which he hated, and never understood.

He was not clever at school, failed most of his exams, but did not worry much. He was fairly good at sport, and that satisfied him.

The fact that he might have to earn his living was, then, a problem outside his orbit!

When he left Victoria College, with a rather inglorious record, he was a problem-boy to his family.

"What shall we do with Kenny?" became the household slogan.

Kenny decided the matter for himself. He would follow in his father's footsteps, and become an engineer.

He was packed off to an engineering works in Shrewsbury, as an apprentice, where he discovered you have to know even more about maths than in doctoring.

Realizing that he would never make an engineer, he went home, with only vague ideas about his future. His father died about this time, which made it all the more important for the young More to make up his mind. He had an idea he would become a trapper, in Canada. He had read lots of books about the exciting life of trappers and, moreover, he had a friend who wanted to go with him.

By now his family, that is, his mother, his grandmother, his aunts and cousins, were so tired of the problem "What shall we do with Kenny?" that between them they found the £200 for the fares of Kenneth and his friend.

There were lots of complications, his friend became engaged, and, instead of becoming an Empire Builder, Kenneth decided to earn his living at home in Britain.

An old friend of his father was Vivian Van Damm, then producer at the Windmill Theatre in London, and the only man Kenneth knew who would be likely to give him a job.

Mr Van Damm and Kenneth first met when Kenneth was crawling round the nursery floor at Gerrard's Cross. A generous, friendly character, Van Damm found a job for Kenneth's sister, Kate, in the box office at the Windmill.

Then he gave Kenneth a job as a stagehand, which meant he had a broom in his hand to sweep the stage clean between performances, fetched and carried for the players, and any other jobs that happened to come along.

One of Kenneth's serious rôles was as Douglas Bader, the leg-less hero of the sky.

It was a happy-go-lucky life. Sometimes stagehands were told to go on stage, to help out in sketches, and one day More came in for a job as 'feed' to the comedian, Gus Chevalier.

Another time it happened that one of the players had broken his ankle and could not appear. Mr Van Damm, with a twinkle in his eye, looked at the sandy-haired Kenneth and told him: "You go on . . . and do something . . . sing . . . or *ad lib*, till we get the next act ready . . . keep the audience amused!"

Kenneth jumped to it. He knew enough to realize that whatever happened 'the show must go on'.

He had just three minutes to get into the costume of a Beefeater. When the curtain rose the audience saw an odd character in a costume three sizes too big, with a moustache at an angle of 45 degrees. There was a shocked silence for about three minutes. Then Kenneth sang a song, intentionally off-key.

That brought roars of laughter, and he became part of the programme.

Success as a comic was not enough for Kenneth. He had now made up his mind that he wanted to be an actor. He talked to a lot of other boys and girls in the same predicament, who had no money for the training at R.A.D.A.

More answered an advertisement in a theatrical paper, for a job with the Newcastle Repertory Company.

He got the job, and this was really the foundation of his career as an actor. But he discovered that his audience was more interested in the fish and chips they brought to the theatre, and in talking about football than in watching the plays!

However, he learned there the basic rule that an actor must never dry up or stand helpless if he forgets his words – that he must be able to *ad lib*, or make up nonsense as he goes along, just ANYTHING to keep an audience amused.

All this was happening in the summer of 1939, before the start of World War II interrupted his career.

Like many others, Kenneth More realized there was going to be trouble, and volunteered for the Navy.

He became Able-Seaman More, in charge of a gun on a Merchant Ship, with strict instructions NOT to fire unless he really had to. The Navy was then rather short of ammunition, and it had a lot of novices who could have done much unnecessary damage.

When the Day of Emergency arrived, when the ship was attacked by the German Navy, Kenneth went to work in a big way. He did all the right things, according to rule, but the shell stuck halfway, and was never fired!

It was not his fault, and he lived to tell the story, but it was a long time before he lived **down** the incident among his shipmates.

He served later in Cruisers in the Mediterranean,

The life of a star is not all glamour – as Kenneth More shows in this amusing sequence in 'Raising a Riot'.

without much incident, and in aircraft carriers in the Pacific during the last bombardment of Japan.

After the war, he was back in London, demobilized with the rank of Lieutenant and a gratuity of £143, and one idea only in his mind – to pick up his acting career where he had left off before the war.

He made the usual trek of aspiring actors, up and down the shabby staircases of agents' offices, and one day found himself sitting beside Dirk Bogarde, then just demobbed from the Army. Both were hoping for jobs. The play that was being cast at the moment was 'Power Without Glory'. They both got parts that enabled them to eat regularly, and, what was more important, became friends for life. It was not mere coincidence that they co-starred later, in 'Doctor in the House'. They wanted it that way!

Success for More was on the way.

Noel Coward saw 'Power Without Glory' and telephoned the theatre one night, leaving a message for Kenneth, which resulted in a part for him in the Coward play 'Peace in Our Time'.

That was the turning point for More. He did well in the play, and he was also beginning to work in films. His film début is important. He played Lieutenant E. R. G. R. Evans, in 'Scott of the Antarctic'. This was the man who took command after the death of Scott during the British Antarctic Expedition of 1909-13, and who later became known as Evans of the Broke, on account of his heroic exploits during the first World War.

Then there came a day when, playing golf with

Muriel Pavlow played the girl Douglas Bader met and married in 'Reach for the Sky'.

Roland Culver, the idea came up that Kenneth could play the lead in Terence Rattigan's play 'The Deep Blue Sea'.

He played the part on the London stage, and in the film was a great success.

Kenneth More likes flying and is happy spending some of his free time at London Airport or any other airfield he happens to be near, just watching the planes land and take off.

It was his interest in flying and in the men who fly aeroplanes that attracted him to 'Reach for the Sky'.

He had read Paul Brickhill's book, like most of us, when it was published. Like a few of us he knew that Bader flew the Spitfire that led the Battle of Britain Fly-Past over London, in 1945, and he considered Bader as a hero of the first water.

He was flattered when the idea of his playing Bader on the screen was suggested, but he was really more flattered to be beaten, on a golf course, by Bader in person!

"He's better with his tin-legs than a guy with two flesh-legs and a lot of training from professionals," he said afterwards.

Maybe it is hero-worship.

Maybe it is just the fact that Kenneth More likes men for their achievements, their conquest of what-might-have-been failure . . .

Human sympathy is one of the livelier qualities in Kenneth More.

Another More success came with the 'Deep Blue Sea'. Here he is with co-star Vivien Leigh, relaxing after shooting a winter sports scene.

DIRK BOGARDE
The Star who shuns the bright lights

WRITTEN BY MAUD MILLER AND ILLUSTRATED BY BILL DOWSETT

BY PROFESSION Dirk Bogarde is an actor, and by merit a star well up the ladder of success. But once out of the studio the star becomes the individual, shunning all the things most closely associated with the screen – glamour, publicity, extravagant parties, extravagant dress and even more extravagant behaviour.

Unlike most of his fellow actors he hates attending star-studded premieres – even his own! These he prefers to see at a 'sneak view', thus avoiding the dazzling arc lamps and flashing cameras – to say nothing of the inevitable mobbing crowds who throng the pavements at a smart West End premiere.

Not for Dirk the bright city lights or the late night cabarets. He prefers to do his entertaining at home. In fact, his is a quiet, almost retiring nature. Once the dust of the studios is shaken from his feet he likes nothing better than to sink into the obscurity of private life and pursue his own special interests. Perhaps it is not the usual pattern of stardom, but for Dirk it is essential that in his leisure hours he should be himself *not* the star.

He is none the less a top ranker for that! His sense of humour, backed by a good business head, genuine talent, and a fairly tough experience of life all add up to the 'star' label. And one of Dirk's most useful qualities is the wide range of his talent. For example, the role of Lawrence of Arabia – one of his personal heroes – is a far cry from the lighter and more hilarious Dr Sparrow roles that helped to hoist him to stardom.

Born in Hampstead in 1920, he is a mixture of Dutch and Scots. His mother was the Scottish actress Margaret Niven before she married artist van den Bogaerde, a Dutchman who later became art editor of *The Times*.

The van den Bogaerdes can trace their ancestry right back to Anne of Cleves, one of the less unfortunate of Henry VIII's wives.

Dirk simplified the spelling of his name quite early in his career out of sympathy for those who weren't sure how to pronounce the cross-Channel version.

His early schooling was in Glasgow, at the Alan Glens College and afterwards at University College, London.

The son of an artist, Dirk inherited some of his father's talent (at least 2 of his D-Day sketches are in the British Museum and another two sold to America). It was not unnatural therefore that he should always have had his eye on an artistic career, and at fifteen began studying commercial art, and stage and film decor at Chelsea Polytechnic. A year later he won a scholarship to the Royal College of Arts.

Two years of intensive study there, and the young man of eighteen decided to find a practical way of allying his knowledge to a little hard cash, so he got himself a job at the 'Q' Theatre. Here he learned what life in the theatre is really like – and he learned it the hard way, performing the duties of glue boy, tea boy and call boy. In fact, he was general dogsbody!

These early efforts were not without their reward. Promotion to the position of Stage Manager came his way – with an understudy's part thrown in.

That was in J. B. Priestley's "When We Are Married". Luck was with him, for his principal fell ill one night, and Dirk made his professional debut.

Of this landmark he says "That was a highlight in my life . . . my wages rocketed from seven and six to twenty-one shillings a week!''

After this promising beginning another part soon came his way. Again a Priestley play; this time at the Amersham Repertory Theatre. It was while playing here that Dirk first cherished a dream that was later to come true – to have his own home in Buckinghamshire.

But much was to be learned and much was to happen before the desire was fulfilled. War came and Dirk joined up. He was first posted to an Army Intelligence Photographic Interpretation Unit. Then came D-Day, when he was able to make sketches of the scene on scraps of blotting paper. Still progressing in his military career, he was appointed A.D.C. to the Commanding Officer of the 23rd Division, and was also given the job of editing a Forces newspaper.

At the end of the war years he was demobbed with the rank of Major but, ever the modest man, he would

Not for Dirk the star-studded premieres. He prefers informality in his leisure hours.

hate to be addressed as "Major" today. He still looks on his rapid promotion in the Army as something that happened to lots of other young men during the war.

With the end of soldiering came the not-so-easy task of getting back into the theatre. There was no time to lose after his five years' service. But the going was hard, and – with all the other demobbed actors – he began the regular tramp up the stairs to agents' offices. This he did without success for about a year. Then he got the chance that put him on the road to stardom.

Many are the stories of out-of-work actors – so impoverished that they must go hungry, or save their one remaining pair of shoes for extra important occasions. In all honesty it must be said that Dirk Bogarde never swelled their ranks. With his army gratuity and an amiably disposed family only too ready to save him from the role of the 'starving actor', he was spared being too hard pressed.

Indeed, it was his ambition rather than his material well-being that was hard pressed in the search for a suitable break.

Eventually he got a chance – and grabbed it with both hands. The play was "Power Without Glory", and the playwright the then unknown Michael Clayton-Hutton. Also in the cast was another figure well known today – Kenneth More, also re-gearing after the war.

The play was a success, and moved into the West End. From that move the film career of Dirk Bogarde began and advanced with amazing speed.

Producer Ian Dalrymple was in the audience one night and, impressed by Dirk's performance, signed him for the lead role in "Esther Waters", with a Rank contract attached.

Once embarked on films Dirk had good reason to bless his army training more than once, but especially when he played the part of a speedway rider in "Once a Jolly Swagman". Fortunately for him, when he first joined up and before he got his commission in the Photographic Interpretation Unit, he had learned a lot about motor bikes and their tricks, as a despatch rider. Thanks to this previous experience he was able to complete the film without too much trepidation.

So happily did he fit into 'tough' parts that there was a period when it looked as though Dirk would wear a shabby raincoat throughout his film life, and be forever on the run from justice, being tough or hunted or involved in blackmail . . . but Doctor Sparrow saved the day and helped to swing the pendulum of his talent in the direction of versatility, with the accent on comedy.

"Doctor at Sea," incidentally, was his twenty-first film in seven years, which was pretty good going, especially if you consider that he also appeared in a number of stage plays during those seven years.

He did other things, too . . . not the least satisfying being to acquire his dream house in Buckinghamshire – dating back to the fifteenth century, and alleged to have been used as one of Cromwell's H.Q. during *his* war.

The house was somewhat derelict when Dirk bought it, and most of its beauty to-day is the result of his own

Dirk's busy days start at his desk, answering the formidable piles of mail coming in from all over the country.

On location while filming 'The Spanish Gardener', Dirk enjoys a free moment in a fishing boat.

hard labours, with help from weekend guests, who were apt to find themselves pushed into denims, and issued with paintbrush or spade.

Since Cromwellian days there have been many alterations and additions to the place, and with his artist's instinct Dirk has rather cossetted the atmosphere, without the too obvious glare of modernising, except where the plumbing and heating is concerned. Why not have comfort decently, is his argument.

Many of the lovely pieces of furniture are the rewards of patient trailing round local auction sales. There is, for example, a satinwood spinet with red silk. It is believed to be the second only of its type in existence. The first was made specially for Queen Victoria. Another time he found an old oak dresser, and had to haggle with the auctioneer on the price. He got it for £8 in the end.

If Buckinghamshire is rich in old furniture it is also a good place for riding. Dirk likes horses, understands them, and has an eye for a 'likely character' when he goes to horse sales. It is, therefore, hardly surprising that he quickly acquired a stable of fine horses which he not only rides but treats as friends.

Fast cars, too, have his wholehearted admiration and approval, not so much for the thrill of driving them, but because of their efficiency, and because they get him to the studios on time in the morning, or to the theatre in the evening.

Among other things he enjoys collecting are unusual vessels to hold the flowers from his garden. One of his prize pieces is an old Victorian footbath (an unlikely object at the best of times) picked up at an auction for a few shillings. Surprisingly, it makes a perfect setting for a display of hyacinths grown from bulb-stage.

Yet another domestic partiality is for cats and dogs. When he first settled at his Bucks home, a Chinchilla cat was bestowed on him by Sally Anne Howes. A Siamese was added later, as well as a variety of dogs.

One very important sector of the Bogarde dwelling is the place where he keeps his records. He has literally hundreds of them.

When he was first asked to 'disc-jockey' for the B.B.C. he said he would like the programme to be called 'I Play What I Like', and astonished the critics by doing just that, without any indulgence in favour of 'pops'.

That was a bit of the real Bogarde, to go out on a limb, choosing what he personally enjoyed, some sentimental, some nostalgic, all of them good music, introduced with simplicity.

That is typical of Dirk, the independent man, who won't have a telephone in his house!

For all he is a star, Dirk Bogarde has the endearing virtue of humility, and once told me that the weekly income of a secretary would serve him quite adequately. This was not just an exaggerated statement for the record. He could live perfectly happily on the most modest income, for he sets more store on his own personal freedom than on money.

He has turned down innumerable Hollywood propositions for films which promised huge sums of money. His rejection was partly because he did not care for the scripts, and partly because, as a valued star of the Rank Organisation, he encounters no trouble at all in suggesting just which films he would like to make.

As the reluctant hero of the film world, who must be the publicity agent's nightmare, Dirk has proved over and over again that even if it pays to advertise, when you have real talent sometimes it pays *not* to advertise!

DENNIS LOTIS

The Star who takes chances

Written by

A. DEVESON & B. WACE

Illustrated by

BILL DOWSETT

"MY life's been made up of taking chances," says handsome, dark-haired Dennis Lotis. And if you manage to make him tell the story of his success, you can see what he means.

Dennis, now one of our most likeable 'pop' singers, began his journey to the top when he entered a talent contest at the age of nine. "Let me try," he persuaded his father, a Greek restaurant owner who had settled in South Africa. He carried off first prize and, as a result, piped a popular song over the air in a Johannesburg children's broadcast.

Next step was to run away from school, and at 15 get himself a job as a £4-a-week bus conductor.

Dennis was delighted with his first pay packet, but his father didn't share his enthusiasm. He insisted that if he must leave school, then at least he must embark on a more stable career, and set him up as an electrical apprentice.

"And down went my pay to fifteen shillings," Dennis says ruefully.

But he couldn't get show business out of his system, and long before the four years' apprenticeship was up,

he abandoned it for a £10-a-week job, singing with a cinema organist. From there, in a very short time, he graduated to singing with South Africa's leading bands. Dennis tells how, during this period, he lost a beard and gained a wife. The beard went when he sang on a radio show sponsored by a shaving cream manufacturer! He gained a wife when he was working in a band at a fashion show. One of the model girls, Rena, caught his eye, they became friends, and soon afterwards they eloped.

Dennis could easily have been content to stay in South Africa. He was at the top there; he had a pretty wife, and a nice home. But once again he showed the same restless drive that has carried him along throughout his career. He decided that England must be his next challenge, and to raise money for the journey, he took all he had to the races—and lost it. So he saved up again, until finally he had enough to leave Rena secure and to buy himself a ticket on the boat. He arrived in England with only £25 in his pocket, and a letter of introduction to bandleader Ted Heath.

But Heath was elusive. Undismayed, Dennis managed

instead to meet Henry Hall, won two appearances on his famous 'Guest Night' and, as a result, was heard by Heath, who promptly signed him up as resident vocalist.

"My gamble had paid off," says Dennis.

A record contract followed, and Dennis soon rocketed to fame. With songs like *Don't Let the Stars Get in your Eyes*, he reached the top of Britain's musical polls. Then, with Ted Heath's blessing, he decided to launch out on his own. Dennis says he vividly remembers that day in April, 1955, when he walked on to the stage of Manchester's Hippodrome Theatre—all alone for the first time. Among his numbers was one he had written himself, *The Golden Ring*.

It touched a prophetic note, because Dennis's future continued golden. He was cast for a TV series in *Hit Parade*, then in *The Tin-Pan Alley Show;* he made two films, *The Extra Day* and *It's a Wonderful World*, where he appeared as a guest artist with the Ted Heath Band again, playing the role of—Dennis Lotis. He appeared in his first TV musical, *The Girl Friend*, and was singing lead in a new West End all-British musical, *Harmony Close*. B.B.C. and Rediffusion gave him television shows of his own and, one of the highest accolades of all, he was asked to take part in a Royal Command Performance, singing in front of the Queen. And all the while his records have continued to spin—top successes like *Tammy, I'm the Only Man on the Island*, and another of his own composition, *Valentina*.

But 'pop' singers come and go. Which is maybe why Dennis's constant desire is to get away from the tag, 'Dennis Lotis—singer'.

"It's too insecure," he says. "Take Crosby and Sinatra, for instance. They're wonderful singers, but I doubt if they'd have lasted if they hadn't made names for themselves in films as well. And that's what I want to do—make a name as Dennis Lotis—entertainer."

Looking back on the list of things Dennis has tackled so far, he seems to be going the right way about it. For instance, he followed his successful three weeks' tour as guest artist with Ted Heath's band in America, by plunging into the unknown field of pantomime, and taking the part of the miller's son in *Puss in Boots* at Birmingham.

In achieving his dreams of the future, Dennis has a wonderful partner in his attractive wife, Rena. She has backed him right from those early South African days, when she encouraged him to try his fortunes abroad. "And, like a good scout, agreed to stay at home till I'd made my mark."

Now, apart from being wife to Dennis and mother to their two enchanting sons, Damon and Kim, she acts as his secretary-agent, too. It's Rena who keeps his engagement book up to date, deals with his business correspondence, safeguards his privacy and, in fact, gives Dennis the peaceful home life that he needs to soothe the strain of every performance. No wonder he looked so relaxed in shows like *Six-Five Special* as he sang, pipe in hand, and wandered across the floor.

Dennis admits that there was a time when he suffered from nerves. In his early days with Ted Heath he concentrated on slow, romantic ballads, but when drummer-vocalist Jack Parnell left the show, and Ted needed a new beat singer, Dennis volunteered.

"I made myself get out in front and sing numbers like *Cuddle Me,* and *Such a Night*. I wasn't a 'zip' vocalist, and I reasoned I'd be doubly nervous. I knew that if I could overcome it this time, then I'd be all right for the rest of my life."

This story is typical of the determination and intelligence Dennis has continually shown in furthering his career.

At one time, he admits, he was even nervous of his fans—but only the souvenir hunters! They continue to take a heavy toll of bow ties, buttons and handkerchiefs, but now he's philosophical about his losses. Although it can be costly, he says, with ties around a guinea, and silk handkerchiefs ten shillings each! Enclosing photographs with replies to the 500-odd fan letters

Dennis relaxes in the coach while on tour with Ted Heath's band.

that he gets each week is also costly, especially as Dennis insists that it would be mean to continue sending out old pictures, and has frequent photographic sittings at £20 a time.

Rena helps him organize fan mail replies, and keeps in order the row of files on his study desk that she's painted white with dark green drawers. The files are pink to match the pink-painted upright piano, for Dennis and Rena have a love of colour, which is obvious from every room in their modern home in Mill Hill, London. Their big, airy lounge, which is partitioned into a dining-room half and a drawing-room half, has turquoise, deep pink and yellow walls. In the dining-room section, the ceiling is black; in the other, white. One of the gayest places is Damon's and Kim's hideout, with its blue and yellow walls and ceiling, red carpet, curtains with an old crocks motor-car pattern, and bunk beds.

Dennis and Rena have called their home Denree. And just as they have collaborated on the name, so they have joined together in planning the decoration and furnishing. Dennis makes much of the furniture himself; then Rena paints it. For instance, there's a two-tiered coffee table, built by Dennis, and painted Siamese

At home Dennis rehearses at his dashing pink-painted piano. In free moments he teaches his sons to play too.

pink and black by Rena. There's a maple-wood dining table; a shade over the television light which he cleverly adapted from a lantern-shaped hanging shade; a flower-stand, painted yellow by Rena and used for magazines and music.

Dennis finds this handiwork a relaxation. He also enjoys art, and is a talented surrealist painter. One of his pictures with musical instruments as the subject hangs on the yellow lounge wall. Dennis collects classical records—and pipes. He brings a pipe back from every country that he visits. They're hanging, all shapes, all sizes, and all smoked, in the study which Rena says belongs to the Lotis men. For in here is Damon's precious bicycle, and two handsome wood fire-engines that belong to Kim. And here, too, is the dashing pink-painted upright piano on which Dennis rehearses and, in free moments, teaches his sons to play.

Dennis brings a pipe back from every country he visits.

"It'll be interesting to see how they make out," says Dennis, who lists first among his hobbies: "My sons."

Despite all his activities, Dennis finds time to enjoy plenty of sports. He is good at swimming, tennis, golfing and horse-riding. Not very long ago he admitted that he'd like to make a Western.

It all fits in the Dennis Lotis plan— to be not Dennis Lotis, Singer, but Dennis Lotis, Entertainer. He reached the top first in South Africa; now he's at the top in England. Next step is America, and the world. And with his talent, his engaging natural charm, and his drive and determination, we think it won't be long before he makes it.

Make a Tyrolean Belt with Lisa

You will need — ¾ yd of webbing, 2 pieces of felt in red and green, a strip of white lace, yellow cord, and gingham for lining.

FELT

LINING

RUBBER ADHESIVE

First measure your waist like this, then turn in the edges of the webbing and hem.

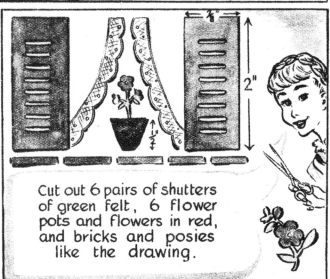

Cut out 6 pairs of shutters of green felt, 6 flower pots and flowers in red, and bricks and posies like the drawing.

Follow the guide, and stick down the felt and lace. Press with heavy books.

Leave the belt to dry firm under the books.

ADHESIVE

PATTERN GUIDE   CENTRE BACK ↓

Now isn't that easy?

Line out the belt, sew on the hooks, and tuck the ends of the cords into hearts cut out of felt. Thread the cord through the hooks.

HE'S LOCKING THE DOOR.

MUST BE TALKING TO THE GIRL. PHEW! SOUNDS LIKE SHE'S A PRISONER!

HE'S OUT OF SIGHT NOW.

HELLO THERE! COME TO A WINDOW. WE WANT TO SPEAK TO YOU—WE'RE FRIENDS!

GO AWAY — PLEASE! I WILL BE IN VERY GREAT TROUBLE.

ARE YOU LOCKED IN?

YES. THE CRAKES KEEP ME PRISONER.

I LIVED WITH MY AUNT, BUT SHE DIED A FEW WEEKS AGO. THE CRAKES WERE HER SERVANTS. MY NAME IS INEZ. NOW YOU GO, PLEASE.

COME AWAY WITH US.

I CAN'T GET OUT. I HAVE TRIED.

WE'LL SOON BATTER A WINDOW DOWN.

CRASH

OUT WITH YOU.

HEY! A WOMAN'S COMING!

IT'S MRS CRAKE!

KEEP LOW SHE MUSTN'T SEE WHICH WAY WE'RE GOING!

YOU'RE SAFE NOW.

AT THE HOUSEBOAT, MISS SCOTT HEARS INEZ'S STORY....

I HAVE NO RELATIONS LEFT IN THIS COUNTRY. YOU SEE, I AM HALF SPANISH.

DO YOU KNOW WHY THE CRAKES BROUGHT YOU HERE AND KEPT YOU HIDDEN?

I'VE A RICH UNCLE IN SOUTH AMERICA. HE'S COMING OVER TO TAKE ME HOME WITH HIM. PERHAPS THEY DON'T WANT THAT TO HAPPEN.

I BET THEY'D SAY YOU WERE LOST— AND CLAIM A REWARD FOR FINDING YOU!

PERHAPS. THEY THREATENED TO PUNISH ME IF I LET ANYONE SEE ME.

I WILL KEEP YOU HERE, INEZ. WHILE I MAKE INQUIRIES.

OH! THANK YOU—THANK YOU!

WHAT'S YOUR UNCLE LIKE?

I DON'T REMEMBER. I WAS SO SMALL WHEN I LEFT SOUTH AMERICA.

MISS SCOTT FINDS THE SOLICITORS WHO ARE DEALING WITH THE AFFAIRS OF INEZ'S AUNT. IT IS ARRANGED THAT INEZ SHALL COME TO MANOR SCHOOL UNTIL HER UNCLE ARRIVES. MEANWHILE THE CRAKES, FEARING TROUBLE, HAVE FLED.

AREN'T YOU EXCITED ABOUT YOUR UNCLE COMING TODAY?

YES. BUT I'LL BE SORRY TO LEAVE MY FRIENDS.

WHAT A WIZARD CAR!

I BET IT'S YOUR UNCLE, INEZ.

HE DIDN'T KNOW ME! AND I'VE SENT HIM LOTS OF SNAPSHOTS!

WE CAN'T BE SURE HE'S YOUR UNCLE...

WHILE IN THE HEAD'S STUDY...

I AM SENOR GARCIA—AND HERE IS A LETTER FROM THE SOLICITORS.

The PURPLE PAGODA

Story by Betty Roland
Drawn by Charles Paine

ANCIENT ANKODIA! LAND OF MYSTERY AND MAGIC, FABULOUS CITIES AND DENSE JUNGLES.

IN THE ROYAL GARDENS THE KING'S SON, TOSALI, PLAYS WITH JENNY, THE ENGLISH GIRL WHOSE MOTHER IS THE YOUNG PRINCE'S GOVERNESS. SUDDENLY MRS. MEDWAY FEELS FAINT.

MAMA, WHAT IS THE MATTER?

I FEEL FAINT. IT MUST BE THE HEAT.

LIE HERE IN THE SHADE. I WILL TAKE CARE OF TOSALI.

THANK YOU, JENNY DEAR

JENNY, LOOK! A PAINTED EMPEROR!

SEE IF WE CAN CATCH IT!

OH! JUST MISSED!

THERE IT GOES!

IT'S GONE RIGHT OVER THE WALL!

WE'LL NEVER GET IT NOW!

WELL, NEVER MIND! NOW WE MUST RETURN TO THE PALACE.

LOOK! THE KING'S SON!

WHAT A PRIZE! IF ONLY WE COULD GET HIM!

BEYOND THE WALL AN ENEMY LURKS..

I HAVE A PLAN. UNWIND YOUR TURBAN. QUICKLY!

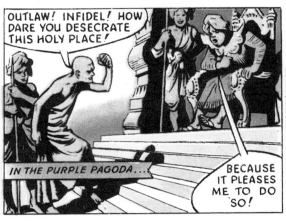

THERE *MUST* BE A WAY TO FORCE THE KING TO COME TO TERMS!

MY LORD, A MESSENGER WITH SPLENDID NEWS!

BID HIM COME HERE AT ONCE.

YOU HAVE THE PRINCE? MY BROTHER'S ONLY SON?

HE WAITS OUTSIDE, MY LORD.

BRING HIM TO ME INSTANTLY, AND TAKE THIS PURSE AS YOUR REWARD.

UNBIND THEIR EYES!

JENNY! JENNY! SAVE ME!

WHAT IS THE MATTER? WHO IS THIS MAN?

HE IS MY UNCLE, A TRAITOR AND AN OUTLAW! HE TRIED TO KILL MY FATHER AND SEIZE THE THRONE!

TAKE THAT, BRAT! YOU MUST LEARN TO CURB YOUR TONGUE!

HOW DARE YOU STRIKE THE PRINCE!

WHO ARE YOU, SPITFIRE?

I'M JENNY MEDWAY, AND I'M HERE TO PROTECT HIS ROYAL HIGHNESS FROM HARM!

NO HARM SHALL COME TO HIM IF MY ROYAL BROTHER GRANTS ME A FULL PARDON AND RESTORES MY TITLES AND ESTATES.

HE WILL NEVER DO THAT! YOU ARE A TRAITOR AND MUST DIE!

SO MUCH THE WORSE FOR YOU, MY DEAREST NEPHEW!

TAKE THEM AWAY AND GUARD THEM WITH YOUR LIVES!

INTO YOUR CAGE, MY LITTLE BIRDS.

DON'T BE AFRAID, TOSALI. I WILL TAKE CARE OF YOU.

THE OUTLAWS REJOICE AT THEIR GOOD FORTUNE.

TO OUR LEADER!

DEATH TO OUR ENEMIES!

HAIL TO THE FUTURE KING!

Just look at those keys. If only I could get them.

THE OTHERS FEAST WHILE WE KEEP WATCH.

WE GET POOR REWARDS FOR OUR SERVICE.

TOSALI! GIVE ME THE JEWEL OUT OF YOUR TURBAN!

HERE IS A REWARD FOR YOU!

IT'S MINE!

NO, MINE!

GIVE IT TO ME!

NO!

WENDY AND JINX

AND

THE RIVAL DUKES

WENDY AND JINX, THE GREAT FRIENDS OF THE FOURTH FORM AT MANOR SCHOOL, ARE TAKING A SUNDAY MORNING WALK ACROSS THE COMMON WHEN THEY HEAR A DOG WHIMPERING...

Story by VALERIE HASTINGS
Drawn by
RAY BAILEY & PHILIP TOWNSEND.

THE POOR CREATURE MUST BE LOST.

HE'S IN SHOCKING CONDITION. LOOK! HE'S BEEN ILL-TREATED, TOO.

GOOD THING I'D SOME CHOCOLATE IN MY POCKET. HE'S STARVING.

WHATEVER CAN WE DO ABOUT HIM?

PETS ARE FORBIDDEN AT SCHOOL. BUT WE MUST DO SOMETHING!

DANGER QUARRY

I KNOW! MISS RICE WILL LOOK AFTER HIM AT HER KENNELS.

CAN'T LEAVE HIM THERE FOR EVER, THOUGH.

WE'LL NOTIFY THE POLICE—AND IF HE'S NOT CLAIMED, I'LL TAKE HIM HOME AT END-OF-TERM. HE'LL LOVE OUR FARM.

AT MISS RICE'S KENNELS...

HE'S A NICE DOG. I'LL SOON HAVE HIM LOOKING LOTS BETTER.

WHAT WILL IT COST?

WINGATE KENNELS

NOTHING — IF YOU'LL SOMETIMES COME AND HELP. MY ASSISTANT'S IN HOSPITAL AND I'M UP AGAINST IT.

IT'S AWFULLY KIND OF YOU.

WE'LL ENJOY IT.

GOOD! NOW LET'S FEED HIM.

THIS IS CHAMPION DUKE OF DARLEY.

HE'S WONDERFUL.

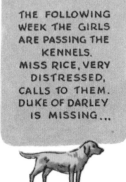

THE FOLLOWING WEEK THE GIRLS ARE PASSING THE KENNELS. MISS RICE, VERY DISTRESSED, CALLS TO THEM. DUKE OF DARLEY IS MISSING...

WHILE MY BACK WAS TURNED SOME WORKMEN LEFT THE PADDOCK GATES OPEN. HE MUST HAVE STRAYED.

SURELY HE'LL KNOW HIS WAY BACK?

THAT'S MISS RICE'S DOG!

AND THEY'RE TAKING HIM AWAY.

THEY'RE MAKING FOR THE KENNELS AT THE SIDE OF THE HOUSE.

COAST'S CLEAR!

CRIKEY! THESE TWO LOOK LIKE TWINS. WHICH IS DUKE OF DARLEY?

DUKE! DUKE, OLD BOY!

GRRRR!

DUKE! DUKE!

HE'S WAGGING HIS TAIL. THIS MUST BE THE RIGHT ONE.

GOOD THING IT'S NOT LOCKED.

USE THIS AS A LEAD.

YES. THE COLLAR SAYS *DUKE*.

NOW LET'S GET OUT OF HERE BEFORE WE'RE SPOTTED.

MISS RICE IS GOING TO BE JOLLY PLEASED WITH US.

BUT NOT WITH MAJOR WILD!

WINGATE KENNELS

HERE HE IS, MISS RICE.

BUT THIS IS MAJOR WILD'S DUKE OF WESTPORT.

GOSH! WE'VE BECOME DOG THIEVES.

BUT I DON'T UNDERSTAND!

THE GIRLS EXPLAIN ALL THAT HAPPENED. AS SOON AS JINX DESCRIBES HOW ONE OF THE TWO DOGS GROWLED WHEN SHE CALLED HIM "DUKE" MISS RICE IS VERY INTERESTED INDEED.

ROBBIE OF RED HALL
in
THE DOG IN THE EMPTY SHIP

Story by George Beardmore
Drawn by Roy Newby

ROBBIE, THE ORPHAN MISTRESS OF FYLE, IS OUT SAILING ONE DAY WITH HER FRIEND DUNCAN. THEY ARE WELL OUT TO SEA, NORTH OF SKYE, WHEN SLOWLY THE WIND DIES AND —

LOSH, ROBBIE, NOT A BREATH OF WIND! IT'LL BE A LONG PULL BACK.

JUST A MINUTE, DUNCAN.

I'VE BEEN WATCHING YON YACHT FOR HALF-AN-HOUR. THERE'S SOMETHING QUEER ABOUT IT.

IT'S BECALMED, LIKE OURSELVES.

NO, IT'S SWUNG ROUND TWICE JUST ANYHOW.

LET'S PULL ACROSS TO IT.

IT'LL MAKE US AWFU' LATE

I DON'T LIKE THIS CALM. IT MEANS SQUALLS, LATER

HARK! CAN'T YOU HEAR SOMETHING?

IT'S A DOG BARKING.

BUT THERE'S NOT A SOUL ON BOARD!

HALLO! ANYBODY ON BOARD?

LOSH, THAT DOG SOUNDS FRANTIC.

MAIDA II

BUT WHERE IS EVERYBODY? THEY CAN'T HAVE BEEN SWEPT OVERBOARD.

THERE'S NO DINGHY TO BE SEEN.

LOSH!

I KNOW WHAT'S HAPPENED!

HE'S CRAZY WITH THIRST.

AND HUNGRY, TOO.

Pedersen
REJAVIK
BEEF ROLL
MADE IN U.S.A

REJAVIK! — WAS HER LAST PORT OF CALL ICELAND?

A PIPE, MADE IN NEW YORK!

BUT THIS, DUNCAN — WHAT'S THIS MAP?

I CAN'T MAKE HEAD OR TAIL OF IT. THE LOG BOOK'S MISSING

THERE ARE NO CLOTHES TO SPEAK OF, NO DINGHY, NO NAME ON THE DOG'S COLLAR — HEY! WHAT'S THAT?

WHATEVER IS IT?

SOME URGENT INSTINCT WARNS ROBBIE —

DUNCAN, QUICK — *THROW IT OVERBOARD!*

AT ONCE THERE IS A MIGHTY UNDERWATER EXPLOSION —

LOSH, A *BOMB!*

YOU SET IT OFF WHEN YOU PICKED IT UP.

IF THE SEA HAD NOT BEEN SO STILL THE BOMB WOULD HAVE GONE OFF BEFORE.

BUT WHAT'S IT ALL MEAN, ROBBIE?

SOMEONE'S CROSSED THE ATLANTIC IN HER AND THEN TRIED TO SINK HER SO THAT — SO THAT *WHAT?*

ONE THING'S CERTAIN, ROBBIE. LOOK AT THOSE CLOUDS!

A SQUALL! CUT OUR BOAT ADRIFT, ROBBIE. WE'LL DOWNSAIL AND TRY TO BRING THE YACHT INTO SHELTER

AND PRESENTLY —

JINGS, MY STRENGTH'S GIVING OUT!

ISN'T THERE A SANDY ESTUARY FURTHER SOUTH? LET'S TRY TO MAKE IT.

MEANWHILE, INSHORE — WHERE'S THIS ESTUARY WE WERE SUPPOSED TO REACH, CHIP?

FOURTEEN MILES DOWNCOAST, SIR.

FOURTEEN MILES! AND A SQUALL BLOWING UP?

IT'S NOT MY FAULT THE WIND DROPPED, IS IT?

QUIT ARGUING AND GET ASHORE!

WHAT ARE YOU DOING, BUD?

POURING PETROL OVER HER SO AS SHE'LL BURN.

THE NEXT TIDE WILL CARRY OFF THE ASHES. WITH THE YACHT GONE, THERE WON'T BE A TRACE OF US LEFT.

HERE COMES THE RAIN!

NO, SIR! THERE'S NOT A BUTTON OF EVIDENCE THAT BUD FLOYD'S SET FOOT ON THESE ISLANDS.

JUST LOOK, BUD!

ISN'T THAT THE MAIDA?

THE *MAIDA'S* AT THE BOTTOM OF THE SEA, DOG AND ALL.

YOU'RE RIGHT, IT *IS* THE MAIDA! I CAN'T MAKE OUT WHO'S SAILING HER. WHAT IN THUNDER STOPPED THE BOMB GOING OFF?

TAKE THIS GUN, CHIP. SHE'S MAKING FOR THE ESTUARY. WHOEVER'S SAILING HER, *FIX* 'EM, AND SINK THE SHIP. UNDERSTAND?

OKAY, BUD. WHERE'LL WE MEET?

AT THAT HOTEL — THE DALLOCH ARMS.

NIGHT'S COMING ON. HE'LL GET 'EM.

YOU'VE FORGOTTEN ONE THING, BUD. THE DOG HATES CHIP. HE LEFT IT THERE TO DIE.

WHILE AT SEA —

AFTER SUPPER, THE TWO FALL FAST ASLEEP, QUITE EXHAUSTED.

BUT ONE OF THE CREW IS NOT ASLEEP.

AND ON THE JETTY...

The *Maida*! This is going to be easy.

ROBBIE, WAKE UP! THE DOG'S HEARD SOMEONE ON DECK.

BACK, ROBBIE! HE'S GOT A GUN!

THAT'S TWICE HE'S SAVED US! THANK GOODNESS HE'S NOT WOUNDED.

WE CAN'T STAY HERE. LET'S FLOAT DOWNRIVER.

WE SHALL BE SAFE THERE. IT'S THE DALLOCH ARMS.

JINGS, I'M DEAD FOR WANT OF SLEEP!

BUT IN THE HOTEL—

IS THAT CHIP?

NO, BETTER STILL IT'S THE *MAIDA*! LET'S GET DOWNSTAIRS.

OH, FOR A BED!

WAIT, ROBBIE! HE'S SEEN SOMEONE.

GET RID OF HIM, GERDA! HE'LL GIVE US AWAY.

BUT EVEN NOW THEY CANNOT SLEEP IN PEACE.

THEIR STORY IS SOON TOLD, AND THEN —

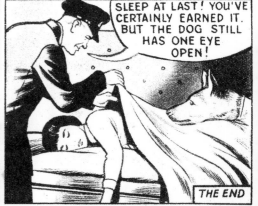

THE END

VICKY
HAS AN
ADVENTURE
IN SPAIN

WRITTEN BY
BETTY ROLAND
DRAWN BY
GERALD HAYLOCK

OH LOOK, DADDY, THERE'S SOME SORT OF FIESTA. CAN WE STAY AND SEE IT?

OF COURSE—IF WE CAN FIND SOME PLACE TO SLEEP.

VICKY AND HER FATHER, PROFESSOR CURTIS, ARE HIKING IN SPAIN. ONE EVENING, AS THEY APPROACH A VILLAGE NEAR SEVILLE, VICKY SEES A TROUPE OF GYPSIES DANCING IN THE STREET.

SORRY, SEÑOR, EVERY ROOM IS TAKEN. IT IS THE SAME EVERYWHERE.

OH DEAR, AND I DID SO WANT TO SEE THE GYPSIES DANCE TONIGHT.

YOUR PARDON, SIR, I COULD NOT HELP BUT OVERHEAR. IF YOU WOULD CARE TO ACCEPT MY HOSPITALITY FOR THE NIGHT...

THAT IS VERY KIND OF YOU.

I HEAR YOU LECTURE AT THE ACADEMY IN PARIS AND I AM HONOURED TO HAVE YOU AS MY GUEST. MY NAME IS DA SILVA, AND MY HOUSE IS YOURS.

IS *THIS* YOUR HOUSE, SEÑOR DA SILVA?

THE HOUSE OF THE DA SILVAS, LET US SAY. MY FATHER HAD IT BEFORE ME; MY SON SHALL HAVE IT WHEN I AM NO LONGER HERE.

PAPA, ARE WE GOING TO THE FIESTA TONIGHT?

DON CARLOS, WHERE ARE YOUR MANNERS? GREET OUR GUESTS AS BEFITS A GENTLEMAN OF SPAIN!

SEÑOR—SEÑORITA, WE ARE HAPPY TO RECEIVE YOU AND TRUST YOUR TIME WITH US WILL BE HAPPY.

LITTLE DON CARLOS, WE ARE DEEPLY HONOURED BY YOUR KINDNESS.

VICKY IS SHOWN TO HER ROOM

THANK GOODNESS I PUT ONE DECENT DRESS IN MY PACK. I HOPE DADDY HAS A CLEAN SHIRT LEFT TO WEAR TO THE FIESTA TONIGHT.

THAT EVENING

ISN'T IT EXCITING? THAT WILD GYPSY MUSIC MAKES ME LONG TO DANCE.

OLÈ! OLÈ!

OH, HOW YOU STARTLED ME.

YOUR PARDON, SEÑORITA. I SAW YOU IN THE WOODS AND CAME TO GIVE YOU THIS.

HOW PRETTY! IS IT SOME SORT OF LUCKY CHARM?

WE GYPSIES SAY IT BRINGS GOOD LUCK TO ANYONE WHO WEARS IT.

HOW KIND OF YOU. I'LL WEAR IT ALL THE TIME.

YOU WERE KIND TO ME LAST NIGHT. THE ROMANIES NEVER FORGET A KINDNESS — OR AN INJURY.

AND NOW I MUST GO. ADIOS, BELLA SEÑORITA. SOMEDAY PERHAPS WE MEET AGAIN.

I HOPE SO. GOODBYE, AND THANK YOU FOR THE LUCKY CHARM.

MEANWHILE, DON CARLOS AND HIS DOG HAVE RUN AHEAD THROUGH THE WOOD...

LUCA! LUCA, WAIT FOR ME! COME BACK!

YAP! YAP! YAP!

WHERE HAS LUCA GONE TO? HE SEEMED TO DISAPPEAR BEHIND THIS ROCK. LUCA! LUCA!

WHY, HERE'S A SORT OF CAVE. HE MUST HAVE GONE IN AFTER THE RABBIT. LUCA! LUCA! I BELIEVE I CAN HEAR HIM.

LUCA! LUCA! WHERE ARE YOU? WHAT A STRANGE PLACE THIS IS. IT SEEMS TO GO RIGHT INTO THE SIDE OF THE HILL.

SUDDENLY THE ROOF OF THE CAVE CRASHES DOWN BEHIND HIM.

OH-H-H-H! THE CAVE HAS FALLEN IN! I CAN'T GET OUT! I'M SHUT IN! OH-H-H-H!

DON CARLOS! DON CARLOS! WHERE ARE YOU?

OH, WHATEVER SHALL I DO? I CAN'T FIND HIM ANY-WHERE!

AFTER A FRUITLESS SEARCH, VICKY RETURNS TO THE CASTLE.

VICKY, WHAT'S THE MATTER?

DON CARLOS HAS DISAPPEARED! I CAN'T FIND HIM ANYWHERE.

WHAT!

CALL EVERY SERVANT ON THE PLACE! SEARCH EVERY INCH OF THE GROUNDS UNTIL YOU FIND HIM!

SI, SEÑOR, WE GO AT ONCE!

WHAT IS THAT YOU'RE WEARING ROUND YOUR NECK?

IT'S A LUCKY CHARM! THE GYPSY BOY GAVE IT TO ME THIS MORNING.

GYPSY! WHEN WAS THIS? WHERE DID YOU SEE HIM!

IN THE WOODS. BUT HE DID NOT TOUCH DON CARLOS, I SWEAR IT!

OUT OF MY WAY! I KNOW THESE PEOPLE BETTER THAN YOU DO AND BY HEAVEN, IF THEY'VE HURT MY SON, THEY SHALL PAY FOR IT DEARLY!

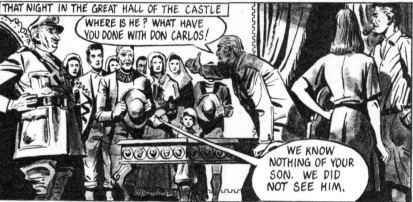

THAT NIGHT IN THE GREAT HALL OF THE CASTLE

WHERE IS HE? WHAT HAVE YOU DONE WITH DON CARLOS!

WE KNOW NOTHING OF YOUR SON. WE DID NOT SEE HIM.

TAKE THEM AWAY, CAPTAIN. SEE THEY NEITHER EAT NOR DRINK UNTIL MY SON IS FOUND.

SI, SEÑOR.

DADDY, ALL THOSE INNOCENT PEOPLE TO BE MADE TO SUFFER! IT'S HORRIBLE!

UNABLE TO SLEEP, VICKY WANDERS THROUGH THE MOONLIT WOOD

I MUST FIND DON CARLOS. LITTLE GYPSY CHARM, TELL ME WHERE TO LOOK SO THAT I CAN SET NANDO AND HIS PEOPLE FREE!

WHAT'S THAT? I THOUGHT I HEARD A DOG WHINING. IT SEEMED TO COME FROM BEHIND THAT ROCK. THERE IT IS AGAIN! I BELIEVE IT'S LUCA!

LUCA! LUCA, WHERE ARE YOU? THERE SEEMS TO BE A KIND OF OPENING, A CAVE! DON CARLOS! DON CARLOS, ARE YOU THERE?

VICKY! WHAT ON EARTH ARE YOU DOING?

DADDY LISTEN! I'M SURE I CAN HEAR LUCA BARKING RIGHT BEHIND THOSE STONES AND ROCKS.

BY JOVE, YOU'RE RIGHT! THEY'RE TRAPPED BEHIND THE FALL OF ROCKS AND EARTH.

QUICKLY! BACK TO THE CASTLE. WE MUST GET A TEAM OF MEN TO DIG THEM OUT.

HALF AN HOUR LATER

SEÑOR, IT WILL TAKE DAYS TO CLEAR AWAY THESE TONS OF ROCK AND EARTH.

IMPOSSIBLE! THE BOY MAY BE INJURED. HE WILL DIE UNLESS WE RESCUE HIM AT ONCE.

IF WE COULD ONLY FIND SOME OTHER ENTRANCE TO THE CAVES!

I KNOW! THE GYPSIES, THEY WILL KNOW. SEÑOR DA SILVA, YOU MUST ASK THEIR HELP.

SI, SI, THE GYPSIES WILL KNOW!

AND SO

CAVES? YES, I KNOW ALL OF THEM, LIKE THE LINES ON MY HAND.

THEN FIND MY SON, AND YOU WILL BE RICHLY REWARDED.

THIS IS ANOTHER WAY IN. I MUST HAVE ROPES AND LIGHTS. THE WAY IS DEEP AND DARK.

FETCH HIM ANYTHING HE ASKS FOR, AND BE QUICK ABOUT IT.

NANDO DISAPPEARS INTO THE CAVES AND THE OTHERS WAIT IN DESPERATE ANXIETY.

HE'S BEEN GONE AN HOUR. WHAT CAN HAVE HAPPENED TO HIM?

IF HE DOESN'T COME SOON I'LL GO AFTER HIM.

BUT SUDDENLY, THROUGH THE TREES.

PAPA! PAPA!

CARLOS, MY SON! YOU ARE SAFE AND WELL! HEAVEN AND ALL THE SAINTS BE PRAISED!

YAP! YAP! YAP!

NANDO, HOW DID YOU GET HERE? WHERE HAVE YOU COME FROM?

THERE IS MORE THAN ONE WAY OUT OF THE CAVES, SEÑOR. I KNOW THEM ALL.

THE DA SILVAS HAVE LIVED HERE FOR CENTURIES AND NEVER KNEW THAT THERE WERE CAVES ON THEIR ESTATES.

THEY SHOULD HAVE ASKED THE GYPSIES, SEÑOR!

A GREAT FIESTA IS HELD TO CELEBRATE THE RESCUE OF THE LITTLE DON CARLOS.

SEÑORITA, MAY I ASK THE HONOUR OF A DANCE WITH YOU?

INDEED YOU MAY, NANDO!

HONOURED LADY OF THE GYPSY PEOPLE, WOULD YOU FAVOUR ME?

SI, SI, LORD OF THE DA SILVAS, IF YOUR FEET ARE NIMBLE!

OLÈ! OLÈ! HO! LA!

AND SO, TO THE SOUND OF SONG AND DANCING, THE CLICK OF **CASTANETS** AND MUSIC OF GUITARS, WE REACH THE END OF VICKY'S ADVENTURE IN SPAIN. *The End*

STUDYING YOUR NURSING NOTES, SUSAN?

NO—GETTING READY FOR THIS AUDITION.

HOSPITAL QUIET PLEASE

BUT YOU'RE LEARNING THE WRONG BIT. IT ISN'T FROM ACT I—IT'S FROM ACT III —HERE.

I MUST HAVE MISREAD THE NOTICE-BOARD— THANKS A LOT.

MAX AND RODERICK HOLD THEIR AUDITIONS.

WHY DO YOU LEAVE YOUR NEW-WEDDED LORD?

THE GYPSIES CALLED, MY LORD, AND I MUST GO.

WELL, THAT WAS PRETTY GOOD —EH, MAX?

WAIT TILL YOU'VE HEARD SUE—BEFORE WE DECIDE.

HERE I AM, MAX.

WHY DO YOU LEAVE YOUR NEW-WEDDED LORD?

I—I—SORRY, I DON'T KNOW THIS BIT.

HEAVENS—GIRL! WHY DO YOU APPLY FOR A PART IN THE PLAY IF YOU CAN'T EVEN BE BOTHERED TO LEARN THE LINES! THE OTHER GIRL GETS THE PART!

I'M SORRY, MAX—I MUST HAVE LEARNED THE WRONG PIECE OF THE PLAY.

NURSE HARPER GOT IT RIGHT—BUT NEVER MIND —YOU CAN BE HER UNDERSTUDY.

A FEW DAYS LATER...

I'M GOING OFF TO REHEARSAL, NURSE MARSH—SO YOU'LL HAVE TO CLEAR UP THE DRINKS.

ALL RIGHT. BUT THIS PATIENT HASN'T HAD HIS DRINK YET.

HERE—TAKE IT— DON'T JUST STARE AT IT LIKE THAT.

YOU HAVE TO TALK TO HIM GENTLY—DON'T STARTLE HIM.

THE END

VALENTINES SENT TO A YOUNG GIRL OVER A HUNDRED YEARS AGO

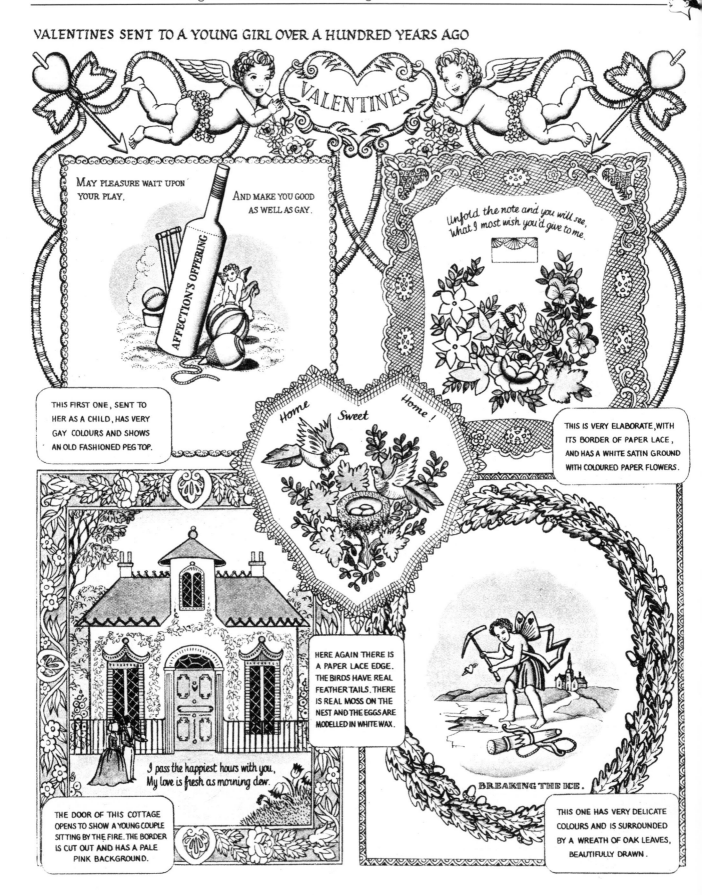

VALENTINES

MAY PLEASURE WAIT UPON YOUR PLAY,

AND MAKE YOU GOOD AS WELL AS GAY.

AFFECTION'S OFFERING

Unfold the note and you will see, what I most wish you'd give to me.

THIS FIRST ONE, SENT TO HER AS A CHILD, HAS VERY GAY COLOURS AND SHOWS AN OLD FASHIONED PEG TOP.

Home Sweet Home!

THIS IS VERY ELABORATE, WITH ITS BORDER OF PAPER LACE, AND HAS A WHITE SATIN GROUND WITH COLOURED PAPER FLOWERS.

I pass the happiest hours with you, My love is fresh as morning dew.

HERE AGAIN THERE IS A PAPER LACE EDGE. THE BIRDS HAVE REAL FEATHER TAILS. THERE IS REAL MOSS ON THE NEST AND THE EGGS ARE MODELLED IN WHITE WAX.

BREAKING THE ICE.

THE DOOR OF THIS COTTAGE OPENS TO SHOW A YOUNG COUPLE SITTING BY THE FIRE. THE BORDER IS CUT OUT AND HAS A PALE PINK BACKGROUND.

THIS ONE HAS VERY DELICATE COLOURS AND IS SURROUNDED BY A WREATH OF OAK LEAVES, BEAUTIFULLY DRAWN.